GCSE

Physics

for CCEA

second edition

REVISION BOOK

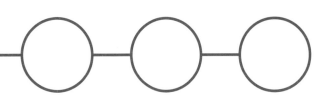

Roy White

HODDER
EDUCATION

The Publishers would like to thank the following for permission to reproduce copyright material:

Photo credits page 77 © Hans F. Meir/istockphoto.com

Acknowledgements CCEA GCSE Sciences Compendium 2000–2011 © CCEA with the permission of the Northern Ireland Council for the Curriculum, Examinations and Assessment.

Orders: please contact Bookpoint Ltd, 130 Milton Park, Abingdon, Oxon OX14 4SB. Telephone: (44) 01235 827720. Fax: (44) 01235 400454. Lines are open 9.00 – 5.00, Monday to Saturday, with a 24-hour message answering service. Visit our website at www.hoddereducation.co.uk

© Roy White 2012

First published in 2012 by

Hodder Education,

An Hachette UK Company

338 Euston Road

London NW1 3BH

Impression number	5	4	3	2	
Year	2016	2015	2014	2013	2012

Cover photo © Dick Luria/Science Photo Library

Illustrations by Datapage

Typeset in Cronos pro 12 points by Datapage India Pvt Ltd

Printed in India

A catalogue record for this title is available from the British Library

ISBN: 978 1444 172850

Contents

Answers to Revision Questions are online:
www.hodderplus.co.uk/cceagcsescience

Introduction

The purpose of this revision guide is to help students who are taking GCSE Physics or the Physics component of Double Award Science fulfill their potential in the course. The book outlines key physics facts and explains the underlying concepts in an approachable style. Particular attention is paid to topics and types of questions that have traditionally caused most difficulty.

As well as helping with knowledge and understanding, the book will give useful guidance in examination techniques in the form of Exam tips. Many of the tips highlight common misconceptions and mistakes made by students during examinations. They also explain how to use the correct terms and critical words to maximise the student's marks.

Using a carefully planned revision strategy which incorporates the reinforcement of core knowledge and essential understanding, this book will assist you to achieve your very best, whether you are striving to obtain an A or A* grade, or hoping to achieve a Grade C. This book is intended to complement its companion text, *GCSE Physics for CCEA (Second Edition)*. The fifteen short chapters are arranged to help you **revise in short chunks**. In each chapter the most important points in each topic are explained and understanding is built up through the use of questions and typical answers. At the end of each chapter there are revision questions (without answers) which can be used for testing knowledge and understanding. The answers to these questions can be found on the website www.hodderplus.co.uk/cceagcsescience

Advice on preparing for examinations

The most important piece of advice is **prepare, prepare, prepare.** But how do you prepare? There is a document issued by CCEA for your benefit. It is called the **subject specification** and it gives detailed information about what you must know, understand and be able to do. The examiners are bound by it! No examiner is permitted to set any question that lies outside the specification. To obtain a free copy, visit the website www.ccea.org.uk and follow the links to qualifications, specifications. The same website gives you access to the **latest GCSE past papers**, **mark schemes** and **Chief Examiner Reports** which provide information for teachers and candidates on candidate performance in each series of examinations.

To help you navigate this revision book some material is in a coloured background. The arrangement is this:

All material not on a tinted background is required for foundation tier students following either the GCSE Double Award Science or the GCSE Physics specifications. All foundation tier material can also be assessed at higher tier.

Material required for the higher tier students following either the GCSE Double Award Science or the GCSE Physics specification is identified with a green tinted background.

Material required for foundation tier students following the GCSE Physics specification is identified with a blue tinted background.

Material required for higher tier students following the GCSE Physics specification is identified with a red tinted background.

But remember, if you are in the slightest doubt about what you must know – look at the specification.

Begin your revision early and make certain there is nothing in the specification that you do not understand. If there is, then ask your teacher. Examiners have a strange knack of asking the questions on topics you didn't get round to revising!

Many pupils fail to maximise their performance because they misread the questions. Remember that examiners can only mark what they see in the paper in front of them, not what they think you meant to write! So read each question carefully and do exactly what you are asked to do.

Assessment objectives (AOs) summarise the knowledge and skills candidates are expected to develop as they follow a GCSE course. The three different assessment objectives are listed in the following table.

AO1	Recall, select and communicate their knowledge and understanding of Physics
AO2	Apply skills, knowledge and understanding of Physics in practical and other contexts
AO3	Analyse and evaluate evidence, make reasoned judgements and draw conclusions based on evidence

AO1 questions – these test your **knowledge and understanding** of the physics content in the specification.

AO2 questions – these involve the **application of skills**. These skills include the **drawing of graphs**, **carrying out calculations** and **applying your knowledge in unfamiliar situations**.

AO3 questions will often involve the presentation of results from an experiment, or a set of data and asking you to **analyse the evidence and make considered judgements** on the evidence provided. AO3 is tested in your unit tests and in the Controlled Assessment Task.

Every physics examination paper, other than the controlled assessment task must test each of AO1, AO2 and AO3. To develop good examination technique in answering AO2 and AO3 questions in particular, it is important that you reinforce your knowledge and skills by practising on examination questions. Examples can be found in this book, in the companion text *GCSE Physics for CCEA (Second Edition)*, or in past examination papers.

QWC questions

Most of the question parts in each examination range from 1 to 3 marks. However, there will be Quality of Written Communication (QWC) questions **worth 6 marks**. While these questions will be testing your ability to communicate physics information in a logical way using appropriate scientific terminology, you can only access the full range of marks available if you understand and describe the Physics involved.

If you are concerned about the mathematical skills you need, look at section 3.4 (GCSE Physics) or section 3.8 (Double Award Science) in the relevant specification and practise these skills by doing the mathematical examples in this book!

If all this seems a little daunting take heart! **The vast majority of GCSE DAS and Physics students are successful** and you are likely to be so too. You have a revision book specially written for the CCEA examinations. It will help you achieve the highest grade of which you are capable. It is now up to you to use it.

1 Force and Motion

Motion in a straight line

The distance between two points is how far they are apart. Displacement measures their distance apart and specifies the direction.

In the same way, speed is the rate at which distance travelled changes with time, but velocity is the rate of change of displacement with time.

$$\text{average speed} = \frac{\text{total distance travelled}}{\text{total time taken}}$$

$$\text{average velocity} = \frac{\text{total displacement}}{\text{total time taken}}$$

Suppose Jo walks around the three sides of the sports pitch shown in the diagram in a time of 250 seconds.

She has travelled a distance of 400 metres. But her final displacement is 200 m to the right of the starting position.

Her average speed is given by:

$$\text{average speed} = \frac{\text{total distance travelled}}{\text{total time taken}} = \frac{400}{250} = 1.6 \, \text{m/s}$$

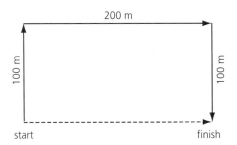

Her average velocity is given by:

$$\text{average velocity} = \frac{\text{total displacement}}{\text{total time}} = \frac{200}{250} = 0.8 \, \text{m/s to the right}$$

If the starting position and finishing position are the same, then the total displacement will be zero and hence the average velocity must be zero also.

Acceleration is defined as the **rate of change of velocity with time**. The definition can be written as an equation:

$$a = \frac{v - u}{t} = \frac{\text{change in velocity}}{\text{time taken}} = \frac{\Delta v}{t}$$

or

$$v = u + at$$

where a is the acceleration in m/s^2
u is the initial (starting) velocity in m/s
v is the final velocity in m/s
t is the time taken in seconds
Δv is the change in velocity in m/s

A positive acceleration means the velocity is increasing, whereas a negative acceleration means a decreasing velocity.

The top table on the next page represents an acceleration of 2 m/s^2. Every second the velocity increases by 2 m/s.

The bottom table represents an acceleration of -2 m/s^2. Every second the velocity decreases by 2 m/s. A negative acceleration is sometimes called a **deceleration** or **retardation**.

Velocity in m/s	13	15	17	19	21
Time in seconds	0	1	2	3	4

Velocity in m/s	19	17	15	13	11
Time in seconds	0	1	2	3	4

Motion graphs

Revised

You need to be able to interpret distance–time and velocity–time graphs to solve questions of a mathematical nature. There are some essential ideas that you must remember:

● The gradient of a distance–time graph represents an object's speed.

● The gradient of a displacement–time graph represents an object's velocity.

● The gradient of a velocity–time graph (or speed–time graph) represents an object's acceleration.

● The area between a velocity–time graph (or speed–time graph) and the time axis represents the displacement (or distance travelled).

Examples

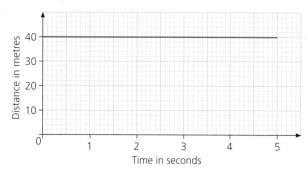

A horizontal line on a distance–time graph means that the body is stationary.

The speed is 0 m/s.

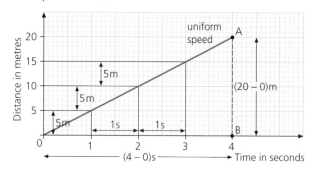

The graph above shows that the distance is increasing by 5 m in every second.

So the speed is 5 m/s.

The gradient of the graph is:
$$\frac{AB}{OB} = \frac{20}{4} = 5\,\text{m/s}$$

Worked example 1

Jim runs home from school each day. The graph shows part of his journey.

a) How far from school is Jim after 15 seconds? [1]

b) What is Jim's steady speed during the first 15 seconds of his motion? [3]

c) Describe the motion during the last 10 seconds of the journey. [1]

d) Calculate Jim's average speed for the entire 25 seconds of the journey. [3]

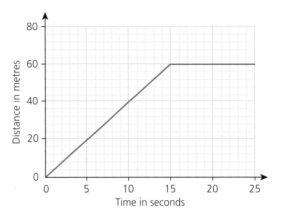

Answers

a) At $t = 15\,s$, distance to school is 60 m

b) speed $= \dfrac{\text{distance travelled}}{\text{time taken}} = \dfrac{60}{15} = 4$ m/s

c) Jim is not travelling for the last 10 seconds.

d) average speed $= \dfrac{\text{total distance travelled}}{\text{total time taken}} = \dfrac{60}{25} = 2.4$ m/s

Worked example 2

The velocity–time graph for a car is shown opposite.

a) What was the change in velocity of the car in the first 5 seconds? [3]

b) Write down the equation that links acceleration, change in velocity and time taken. [1]

c) Calculate the acceleration of the car during the first 5 seconds. [2]

d) Calculate the total distance travelled in 10 seconds. [4]

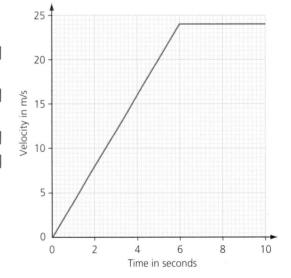

Answers

a) At $t = 0$ seconds, velocity $u = 0$ and at $t = 5$ seconds, velocity $v = 20$ m/s.
So change in velocity $= v - u = 20 - 0 = 20$ m/s

b) $a = \dfrac{v - u}{t}$

c) $a = \dfrac{20 - 0}{5} = 4$ m/s^2

d) Distance travelled in 10 s = area of triangle + area of rectangle under graph
$$= (\tfrac{1}{2} \times 6 \times 24) + (4 \times 24) = 168\,m$$

> **Exam tip**
>
> You should also remember that only on a single straight line part of a velocity–time graph is the average speed equal to the average of the speeds at the start and end of the straight line. Revision question 5 gives an example of finding average speed from a velocity–time graph.

1 a) A cyclist takes 20 seconds to ride from point A to point B, exactly halfway round a circular track of radius 100 m, as shown in the diagram. She travels at a steady speed.

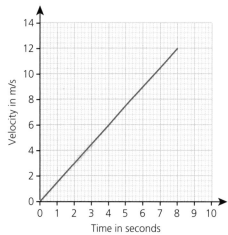
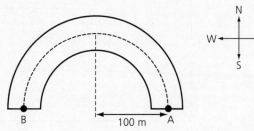

i)   Calculate the total distance travelled by the cyclist.   [2 marks]

ii) At what speed was the cyclist travelling?   [4 marks]

iii) Complete the statement:

When the cyclist reaches the point B her displacement is _____ m to the _____ of A.   [2 marks]

b) The graph below shows how the velocity of a car changes with time.

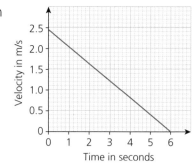

> **Exam tip**
>
> Make sure you know the equations for average speed, average velocity and acceleration. Questions on these topics are favourites with examiners.

i)   Calculate how far the car travels during the 8 seconds of its motion.   [3 marks]

ii) Use the graph to calculate the acceleration of the car.   [3 marks]

2 A graph of velocity against time for a golf ball is shown opposite.

a) Use the graph to find the deceleration of the ball.   [3 marks]

b) How far does the ball travel in 6 seconds?   [3 marks]

3 Maureen cycles to school each day. The graph illustrates her journey.

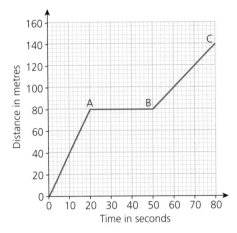

Use the graph to calculate her speed for the last part, BC, of the journey.　　　[3 marks]

4 The table below shows how the speed of a car affected its stopping distance.

Speed in m/s	0	5	10	15	20
Thinking distance in m	0	1	2	3	4
Braking distance in m	0	4	16	36	64
Total stopping distance in m	0	5	18	39	68

　a) Using the table, calculate the reaction (thinking) time of the driver.　　[3 marks]

　b) When the brakes are applied, the car decelerates uniformly to rest. Using the braking distance for a car travelling at 20 m/s, calculate the time it takes from the moment the brakes are applied for this car to come to rest.　　[4 marks]

5 Opposite is a velocity–time graph showing the motion of a train.
　a) How can you tell from the graph that the train is always travelling in the same direction?
　　　　　　　　　　　　　　　　[1 mark]

　b) Calculate the acceleration of the train represented by line AB on the graph.
　　　　　　　　　　　　　　　　[3 marks]

　c) At what time does the train driver first apply the brakes?　　　[1 mark]

　d) Calculate the distance travelled on each of the stages AB, BC and CD.　　[7 marks]

　e) Calculate the average speed of the train over the 225 s of its journey.　　[3 marks]

Exam tip

When solving problems with graphs, always look at the axes labels, units and scales to check that you have read the data correctly.

Go online for the answers　　　　　　　　　　　　　　　Online

2 Motion under Gravity

The Italian scientist Galileo is credited with the discovery that, in the absence of resistive forces such as air resistance, all objects fall to Earth with the same **gravitational acceleration**, g. The value of g is approximately 10 m/s². Likewise, a ball thrown vertically upwards slows down at a rate of 10 m/s². Physicists tend to use the convention that **upwards is positive** and **downwards is negative**, as illustrated in the following examples.

Worked example 1

1   An object falls from rest and strikes the ground exactly 1.5 seconds later. At what speed does it hit the ground?   [3]

2   A ball is thrown vertically upwards with an initial speed of 24 m/s.

    a) How long does it take the ball to reach maximum height?   [3]

    b) What is the maximum height?   [4]

Answers

1   $v = u + at$
    $= 0 + (-10 \times 1.5)$
    $= -15$ m/s (where the minus sign shows the ball is falling)

2   a) $v = u + at$, but at maximum height $v = 0$, so:
       $0 = 24 + (-10t)$, so $10t = 24$
       $t = 2.4$ seconds to maximum height

    b) Average speed $= \dfrac{(u + v)}{2} = \dfrac{(24 + 0)}{2} = 12$ m/s

       Height = average speed × time = 12 × 2.4 = 28.8 metres

Newton's laws

Revised

Balanced forces – Newton's First Law

If the forces on an object are equal in size but opposite in direction, then the forces are said to be **balanced**. If the forces on an object are balanced, then its velocity remains constant. This means that the object will either remain at rest or move in a straight line with a constant speed. This is summed up in Newton's First Law:

> A body stays at rest, or if moving it continues to move with uniform velocity, until an unbalanced force makes it behave differently.

Exam tip
This law must be memorised.

Unbalanced forces – Newton's Second Law

Unbalanced forces cause the velocity of an object to change. This can cause the speed of the object to change or it may cause the object to change the direction of its motion. Newton's Second Law tells us the mathematical relationship between the resultant (unbalanced) force, F (in N), the mass m (in kg) and the acceleration, a (in m/s²).

> $F = ma$

Exam tip
This equation must be memorised.

Worked example 2

The friction force opposing the motion of a locomotive of mass 25 000 kg is 100 000 N.

a) What forward force must the locomotive provide if it is to travel along a straight, horizontal track at a steady speed of 1.5 m/s? [1]

b) What is the acceleration of the locomotive if the forward force increases to 175 000 N and the friction force is unchanged? [4]

Answers

a) Velocity is steady, so forces are balanced:

forward force = friction force

So, forward force = 100 000 N

b) Forward force = 175 000 N

Friction force = 100 000 N

Unbalanced force = (175 000 − 100 000) = 75 000 N

But $F = m \times a$

so 75 000 (N) = 25 000 (kg) × a (m/s^2), which gives

$a = 3$ m/s^2

Forces in pairs – Newton's Third Law

This law states that if body A exerts a force on body B, then body B exerts a force of equal size on body A, but in the opposite direction.

Consider a book of weight 10 N resting on a table. The book (body A) exerts a downwards force of 10 N on the table (body B). But the table (body B) exerts an upwards force of 10 N on the book (body A). It is because these forces are exactly equal in size and opposite in direction that the book remains stationary on the table.

Mass and weight

Revised

Mass is defined as the amount of matter in a body. For the same pushing force, a large mass shows a greater reluctance to change its velocity than a small mass. Physicists call this property **inertia** (from the Latin for laziness!).

Weight is the force of gravity on an object. Since objects close to the Earth all experience the same acceleration, g, we can apply Newton's Second Law to get:

force (of gravity) = mass × acceleration due to gravity

weight = mass × acceleration due to gravity

$W = m \times g$

Exam tip

This equation must be memorised.

On the surface of the Earth the value of g is approximately $10\,m/s^2$. Using this equation we see that a mass of 1 kg on the Earth's surface has a weight of 10 N.

The value of g is roughly the same over the surface of the Earth, but the further you move away from the surface, the smaller g becomes. The Moon has a weaker gravitational field than Earth. On the Moon a mass of 1 kg weighs only 1.6 N.

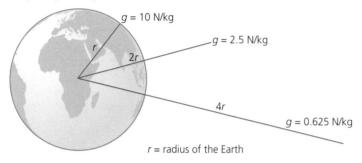

r = radius of the Earth

Worked example 3

a) Calculate the weight of an object of mass 70 kg on Earth.　[2]

b) The same object is taken to the Moon, where $g = 1.6\,m/s^2$. Calculate: i) its mass and ii) its weight on the Moon.　[1]

c) On another planet, a mass of 12 kg weighs 105.6 N. Calculate the value of g on this planet.　[2]

d) Comment on the units for g.　[2]

Answers

a) $W = mg = 70 \times 10 = 700\,N$

b) i) Its mass does not depend on its location – its mass is still 70 kg.

　ii) $W = mg = 70 \times 1.6 = 112\,N$

c) $g = W / m = \dfrac{105.6}{12} = 8.8\,m/s^2.$

d) When we think of g as the acceleration of an object in free-fall close to the planet's surface, then we use the unit m/s^2. When we think of g as the strength of the gravitational field, we use the unit N/kg. The two units are equivalent.

The density of an object is defined by the equation:

$$\text{density} = \frac{\text{mass}}{\text{volume}}$$

Exam tip
This equation must be memorised.

The unit for density is kg/m^3. From time to time you may also see the unit g/cm^3.

Measuring density

The mass of a solid block or a liquid can be found using a top-pan balance. If the solid block has a rectangular shape, its volume can be found as the product of its length, breadth and height. If the solid has a cylindrical shape, its volume is given by π × radius² × height.

If the shape is irregular, then its volume is found using a graduated measuring cylinder by the water displacement method.

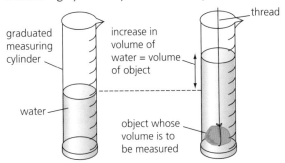

If we want to find the density of a liquid, then we find its volume directly with a measuring cylinder and its mass with a top-pan balance.

A graph of mass against volume is always a straight line through the origin. The gradient of the line is equal to the density. All points on a given line therefore have the same density, as illustrated in the diagram below.

Graphs and density

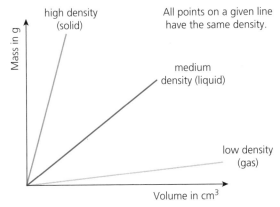

↑ **Graph of mass against volume for three different materials**

The different properties of solids, liquids and gases can be explained using the kinetic theory. The word 'kinetic' means movement and kinetic theory is all about the movement of particles such as molecules and atoms.

Worked example 4

1   One hundred identical copper rivets with a combined mass of 180 g are put into an empty measuring cylinder. When 50 cm³ of water is added, the total volume rises to 70 cm³. Calculate the density of copper.   [4]

2   A mug contains 200 cm³ of hot tea with a density of 1.01 g/cm³. John adds 18 g of sugar, which immediately dissolves. Assuming the addition of the sugar does not increase the volume of liquid in the mug, calculate the new density of the tea.   [4]

Answers

1 Mass of copper = 180 g
   Volume of copper = 70 − 50 = 20 cm^3
   Density = mass / volume

$$= \frac{180}{20} = 9\,\text{g/cm}^3$$

2 Original mass of liquid = volume × density = 200 × 1.01 = 202 g
   Total mass after adding sugar = 202 + 18 = 220 g

   New density of tea = $\frac{220}{200}$ = 1.1 g/cm^3

Exam tip

Density is a new topic for DAS Physics candidates, so it is hard to find examples of past paper questions. But there are lots of them on past GCSE Physics papers. Look them up and do them if you need more practice.

Kinetic theory and density
Revised ☐

Solids	Liquids	Gases
● Molecules vibrate about fixed positions. ● Molecules have strong forces of attraction between them. ● Molecules are packed very close together, so… ● Solids have a high density.	● Molecules can move around in any direction and are not fixed in position. ● Forces of attraction between molecules are still quite strong but not as strong as in solids. ● Molecules are close together but not as close as they are in solids, so… ● Liquids have a medium density.	● Molecules are very, very far apart. ● There are no forces of attraction between molecules, so… ● Gases have a very low density.

Generally, when solids are heated their density decreases as the spacing between the molecules increases. Similarly, when liquids evaporate the density decreases as, once again, the average spacing between molecules increases significantly.

Kinetic theory and changes of state
Revised ☐

The three states of matter are solids, liquids and gases. For example, using the ideas of the kinetic theory we can describe and explain how solids (such as ice) change to liquids (such as water) and how liquids change to gases (such as steam).

● Solids are made up of vibrating molecules.

● Adding heat gives the molecules more kinetic energy, causing more vigorous vibrations.

● As the bonds between the molecules are broken, the solid turns to a liquid.

● As more energy is given to the liquid, more bonds are broken and the free molecules move much faster.

● Those molecules that are fast enough and moving upwards towards the surface can break free of the liquid and become a gas.

Motion in a circle

Consider an object moving at a steady speed in a circle. The direction in which the object is moving is constantly changing, so its velocity is also changing. But if the velocity is changing, the object is accelerating.

The direction of the object's velocity at any instant is along the tangent to the circle at its present location. The direction of the acceleration (and the force causing it) is inwards towards the centre of the circle. The force is called the **centripetal** force. Centripetal means 'centre-seeking'. The size of the centripetal acceleration (and centripetal force) is constant, but its direction is constantly changing as the object moves around the circle.

The size of the centripetal force increases with:

● increasing mass of the object

● increasing speed of the object

● decreasing radius of the circle.

You need to be able to describe how to demonstrate the three points above experimentally. The easy way to do this is to thread a plastic tube with a length of strong thread and tie one end to a rubber bung of known mass and the other end to a newtonmeter.

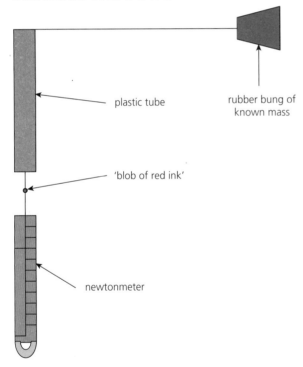

plastic tube

rubber bung of known mass

'blob of red ink'

newtonmeter

Holding the plastic tube in one hand and the ring of the newtonmeter in the other, spin the rubber bung about your head at such a speed that the red ink blob moves neither up nor down. As you do so, the tension in the string will cause the force indicator on the newtonmeter to move. The reading is the force shown on the newtonmeter.

● If you now use a rubber bung of greater mass, but spin it at the same rate as before and at the same radius, the tension in the string will increase.

● If you use the same mass as before and the same thread radius, but spin it faster above your head, once again the tension will increase.

● If you use the same mass as before and spin it at the same rate as before, but at a smaller radius, once again the tension will increase.

The table illustrates common examples of circular (or nearly circular) motion and the causes of the centripetal force.

Example	Cause of centripetal force
Earth orbiting the Sun	Gravitational force between the Sun and Earth
Satellite orbiting Earth	Gravitational force between Earth and the satellite
Car on a circular track	Friction between the tyres and the road
Electron orbiting the nucleus of an atom	Electrical force between positive nucleus and negative electron
Chestnut whirled in a circle at the end of a string	Tension in the string

What would happen if the centripetal force suddenly disappeared? This can happen, for example, if a chestnut is whirled in a circle at the end of a string and the string suddenly snaps. Then the chestnut moves along the tangent to the circle at the point where the string snapped.

Revision Questions

1   The diagram shows the Earth at one particular point in its path around the Sun.

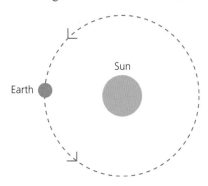

   a) What provides the centripetal force needed to keep the Earth in orbit?   [1 mark]

   b) What is the direction of this force acting on the Earth?   [1 mark]

   c) Copy the diagram and mark the direction in which the Earth is moving
       at the instant shown.   [1 mark]

2   A steel ball of weight 35 N is whirled on a string in a horizontal circle. A bird's eye view of the situation is shown in the diagram.

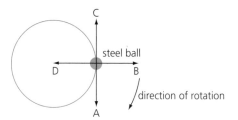

   a) What is the mass of the steel ball?   [1 mark]

   b) What is the name of the force which keeps the steel ball moving in a circle?   [1 mark]

   c) Which letter A, B, C or D gives the direction of this force?   [1 mark]

   d) If the string breaks, in which direction A, B, C or D will the steel ball move?   [1 mark]

   e) The velocity of the ball is **not** constant. Explain why.   [1 mark]

3 Using the ideas of kinetic theory, describe and explain how solids change to liquids **and** liquids change to gases. [6 marks]

> **Exam tip**
>
> Questions on kinetic theory may require you to write a short paragraph rather than just a few words. At least one mark will be for your ability to use the key scientific words correctly, so learn the key words and practise this skill regularly.

4 **a)** Explain what is meant by 'density'. [2 marks]

b) Describe briefly how you could use a measuring cylinder half-filled with water to find the volume of a bracelet. In your description, state what measurements you would make and what calculation you would carry out. [4 marks]

c) A certain bracelet has a volume of $2.4\,cm^3$ and a mass of $46\,g$. Calculate its density. Show clearly how you get your answer. [3 marks]

d) The bracelet is made from a metal that is almost 100% pure.

Use your answer to part **c)** and the table below to find out what the metal is. [1 mark]

Metal	Copper	Gold	Lead	Platinum
Density in g/cm³	8.9	19.3	11.3	21.5

5 The diagram opposite shows an object moving clockwise in a circle.

a) Copy the diagram and draw an arrow to show the direction of the centripetal force acting on the object. Label this arrow F. [1 mark]

b) Draw an arrow to show the direction the object would move if this force were removed. Label this arrow v. [1 mark]

c) What happens to the size of this centripetal force if the mass of the object moving in the circle is increased? [1 mark]

Go online for the answers ──────────── Online

3 Momentum

Momentum is defined as the mass of a body multiplied by its velocity:

> momentum (kg m/s) = mass (kg) × velocity (m/s)

Momentum has size and direction so it is a vector quantity.

Worked example 1

Calculate the momentum of a 1.5 kg football travelling at 12 m/s. **[3]**

Answer

Momentum = mass × velocity = 1.5 × 12 = 18 kg m/s

Momentum conservation   Revised ☐

During your course you will have carried out experimental investigations, possibly using data loggers, or conducted computer simulations on what happens to the momentum of two objects when they collide. You must remember that the results of these investigations show that for objects in collision:

> total momentum before collision = total momentum after collision

This is known as the Principle of Conservation of Momentum and you must be able to apply it to simple collisions.

Worked example 2

1   A trolley of mass 1.5 kg moving at 4 m/s collides with and sticks to a stationary trolley of mass 4.5 kg. Find the velocity of the combined trolleys after the collision. **[4]**

2   A car of mass 1000 kg travelling due north collides with another car of mass 1200 kg travelling due south at 25 m/s. The two cars stick together and immediately after the collision they are moving at 5 m/s due south.

    Find the speed of the 1000 kg car before the collision. **[5]**

Answers

1   Total momentum before the collision = $m \times v$ = 1.5 × 4 = 6 kg m/s
    Total momentum after collision = total mass × velocity of
                                                    combined trolleys
                        = (1.5 + 4.5) × v = 6 × v
    By the Principle of Conservation of Momentum, 6 = 6 × v
    So v = 1 m/s in the same direction as the original trolley

2   Let the speed of the 1000 kg car before the collision be v.
    Let north be the positive direction and south the negative direction.
    Total momentum before collision = $(1000 \times v) + (1200 \times -25)$
    $$= 1000v - 30\,000$$
    Total momentum after collision = total mass $\times$ velocity of
    combined cars
    $$= 2200 \times -5 = -11\,000 \text{ kg m/s}$$
    By the Principle of Conservation of Momentum,
    $$1000v - 30\,000 = -11\,000$$
    So, $1000v = -11\,000 + 30\,000 = 19\,000$
    And $v = 19\,000 \div 1000 = 19$ m/s due north

Impulse–momentum principle

Revised

The definition of momentum and Newton's Second Law can be combined to give a really useful formula.

Since $F = ma$ and, by definition of acceleration, $a = \dfrac{(v - u)}{t}$, we can write:

$F = \dfrac{m(v - u)}{t}$, which when rearranged gives:

$Ft = m(v - u) = mv - mu$ = change in momentum. So,

> change in momentum = force $\times$ time

The product of the force and the time for which it acts (Ft) is called is called the **impulse** of the force. The equation is called the **impulse–momentum principle**.

> **Exam tip**
> This equation must be memorised and is very useful when considering car crashes.

Worked example 3

Suppose a car driver, mass 80 kg, travelling at 72 km/h (45 mph or 20 m/s) collides with a wall and come to rest in a time interval of 0.2 seconds.

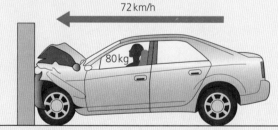

72 km/h

80 kg

What is the average force on the passenger in the collision?   [4]

Answer

Force $\times$ time = change in momentum
    Force $\times$ 0.2 = $80 \times (20 - 0)$
        Force = $\dfrac{1600}{0.2}$ = 8000 N

A force of 8000 N on the driver is potentially lethal. But if the time of impact with the wall were increased to, say, 4 seconds, then the new force on the driver would be given by $F = \dfrac{1600}{4}$ = 400 N. This is a substantial decrease, increasing the probability of the driver surviving the collision.

In an accident like that in the previous worked example, a passenger in a car will tend to continue to move with the speed of the car immediately prior to the collision. This is in accord with Newton's First Law. **Restraining seatbelts** prevent the passenger or driver being thrown through the windscreen and increase the time to come to a stop, thus reducing the force.

Crumple zones are areas at the front and the rear of a car that are designed to collapse relatively easily and slowly. The car's cabin is much stronger, so it does not crumple around the passengers. These crumple zones spread the collisions over a longer time and so reduce the force on the passengers, and hopefully reduce injuries.

Air bags in cars give extra protection in collisions. Front air bags are fitted in the steering wheel or in the dashboard. The shock of a front end collision sets off a rapid chemical reaction inside the bag. The reaction forms a large volume of gas very quickly. The gas fills the bag, which holds a passenger in their seat. The bags are porous and go down quickly after the accident.

Motorway **crash barriers** are designed to prevent vehicles crossing from one carriageway to the other and keep them from impacting or entering roadside hazards. The barriers absorb some of the kinetic energy from the impact caused by the vehicle striking it and redirect the vehicle along the line of the barrier so that it does not turn around, turn over or re-enter the stream of traffic. This is called **containment**.

> **Exam tip**
>
> Don't confuse momentum with the moment of a force. Momentum is mass times velocity, whereas moment is force times distance to a pivot.

Revision Questions — Tested

1 A car sits at rest at the top of a rollercoaster ride as shown.
   The brake is released and the car travels down the slope.

   a) Copy the diagram and mark and label two forces acting on the car when it is moving.

   [2 marks]

   b) At the bottom of the slope the car reaches a speed of 27 m/s and continues along a horizontal track in which a braking system is operated. The deceleration of the car is 6 m/s². Calculate the time taken to come to rest.   [3 marks]

   c) The mass of the car is 1000 kg. The force applied to the car by the braking system is 5000 N. Calculate the additional frictional force provided by air resistance which brings the car to rest.   [3 marks]

2 A sky diver jumps from an aircraft and for a time falls through the air without her parachute open. After a time she opens the parachute.
The graph below shows how the velocity of the sky diver changes as she falls through the air. Her parachute opens at the time marked.

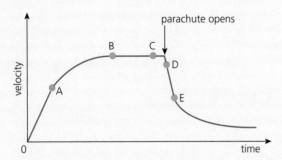

Describe and explain how her acceleration changes in the periods 0A, BC and DE as she descends. In this question you will be assessed on your written communication skills including the use of specialist science terms.   [6 marks]

3 A car travelling at 20 m/s collides with another car. The passenger, who is not wearing a seatbelt, continues to move forward, hitting the dashboard in a collision that lasts 0.1 seconds.
   a) Calculate the value of the force that the windscreen exerts on the passenger's head. Assume the mass of the passenger is 50 kg.   [4 marks]

   b) Explain how a seatbelt would have protected the passenger from serious injury.   [2 marks]

Go online for the answers   Online

4 Energy

Energy forms

Energy forms are the different ways in which energy can appear – such as heat energy, light energy and chemical energy. Energy resources are the different ways of supplying a particular energy form. The table summarises some of the main energy forms.

Energy form	Definition	Examples of resources
Chemical	The energy stored in a substance that is released on burning	Coal, oil, natural gas, peat (turf), wood, food
Gravitational potential	The energy a body contains as a result of its height above the ground	Stored energy in the dam (reservoir) of a hydroelectric power station
Kinetic	The energy of a moving object	Wind, waves, tides
Nuclear	The energy stored in the nucleus of an atom	Uranium, plutonium

↑ Forms of energy

Common energy forms are **heat**, **light**, **sound**, **electrical**, **magnetic** and **strain potential**.

One of the fundamental laws of physics is the **Law of Conservation of Energy**. This states that:

> Energy can neither be created nor destroyed, but it can change its form.

Exam tip
This law must be memorised.

We can show energy changes in an **energy flow diagram**.

What energy changes take place when we strike a match?

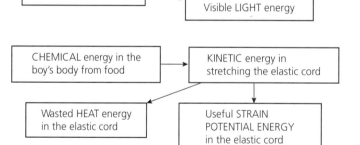

What energy changes take place when we stretch a catapult?

What energy changes take place when we ring an electric bell?

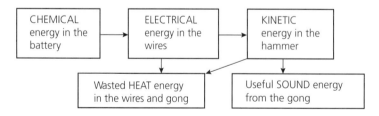

Energy flow diagrams show the main energy changes taking place, but they have **two major limitations**. They usually:

● do not show **all** the energy transformations taking place

● do not show the amount of energy being changed from one form to another.

Energy resources can be classified as renewable and non-renewable. Renewable resources are those that are replaced by nature in less than a human lifetime. Non-renewable resources are those that are used faster than they can be replaced by nature.

Resource	Comment
Solar cells	Solar cells convert sunlight (**solar energy**) directly into electricity. Solar cells are joined together into solar arrays.
Hydroelectric power stations	Water behind a dam (reservoir) contains **gravitational potential energy**. The water is allowed to fall from the dam through a pipe, and it gains **kinetic energy** as it falls. The fast-flowing water falls on a **turbine**, which drives a **generator** to produce **electrical energy**.
Tidal barrage	A tidal barrage is created when a **dam is built across a river estuary**. As the tide rises and falls every 12 hours, water will flow through a gate in the dam. The moving water drives a turbine, which is made to turn a generator to produce electrical energy.
Wave machines	Waves are produced largely by the action of the wind on the surface of water. The wave machine floats on the surface of the water and the **up and down motion** of the water is converted into **rotary motion** of a turbine-generator to produce electrical energy.
Wind turbines	As the wind blows, the large blade turns and this drives a turbine. The turbine drives a generator, which produces electricity. Large numbers of turbines are often grouped together to form a **wind farm**. They can take up a great deal of land, but many are off-shore.
Geothermal power stations	Geothermal power stations use heat from the hot rocks deep inside the Earth. Cold water is passed down a pipe to the rocks. The water is heated by these rocks and the hot water is then pumped to the surface. The steam generated is used to turn a turbine-generator to produce electrical energy.
Biomass	Harvested timber can be dried and turned into woodchips, which are then burned in power stations to produce electricity or sold for solid fuel heating. There are many other forms of biomass. Oil from oil-bearing seeds can be converted into **biodiesel** for road transport.

↑ Renewable resources

Resource	Comment
Fossil fuels	These are **coal, oil, natural gas, lignite** and **peat** (turf). They are burned in power stations to produce steam. This steam drives a turbine, turns a generator and so produces electrical energy.
Nuclear power (fission)	**Large nuclei** (uranium or plutonium) in a nuclear reactor are made to **split** into lighter nuclei by **nuclear fission** with the release of very large amounts of **kinetic energy** in the fission fragments. This energy is used to produce steam, which drives a turbine, turns a generator and so produces electrical energy.

↑ Non-renewable resources

All energy resources except nuclear power and geothermal energy ultimately rely on the energy of the Sun. Most renewable energy resources depend on the weather, which is totally driven by energy from the Sun.

All **biomass** and **fossil fuels** can be traced back to capturing the Sun's energy through **photosynthesis**. Coal, peat and lignite were formed by the action of high pressure and temperature on dead vegetation (such as trees). Oil and natural gas come from the dead remains of animal life (mainly marine life). The formation of all fossil fuels is believed to have occurred over millions of years.

Energy resource	Environmental effect
Fossil fuels	• All release carbon dioxide on burning and so contribute to **global warming**, with consequences such as melting ice-caps, widespread floods and catastrophic changes to the climate. • Burning coal and oil also releases **sulphur dioxide** gas, which causes **acid rain**.
Nuclear fuels	• The waste products will remain dangerously radioactive for tens of thousands of years. • As yet, no one has found an acceptable way to store these materials cheaply, safely and securely for such a long time. • An accident could release dangerous radioactive material, which would **contaminate** a very wide area, such as Fukushima, Japan (2011). • **Decommissioning** – shutting down the power station at the end of its useful life, safely removing the dangerous radioactive waste and returning the site to its former state – is particularly long and expensive, because it requires specialist equipment and personnel.
Wind	• Wind farms use vast areas of land per unit of energy produced. • Many consider them an eye-sore.
Tides	• Tidal barrages can cause habitat problems for marine life and dangers for shipping.
Solar cells	• They are so expensive to produce and easily damaged that many people question whether they result in a net reduction in the use of fossil fuels.
Hydroelectric power (HEP)	• Many HEP schemes involve the flooding of river valleys, causing problems with relocating people and habitat destruction for many plants and animals.

↑ **Effects on the environment**

Primary and secondary sources of information

All of the above information can be obtained from secondary information sources. Part of your course requires you to use primary and secondary information sources.

● **Primary sources** require the learner to interact with the source and extract information. Examples are: interviews with people, e-mail contacts, debates and surveys.

● **Secondary sources** are edited primary sources, i.e. second-hand versions. They represent someone else's thinking. Examples are: books, CD-ROMs, encyclopaedias, magazines and newspapers.

Worked example 1

Certain devices change energy from one form to another. Give the **main** energy changes in the following examples. The first one has been done for you.

a) An electric motor changes *electrical* energy to *kinetic* energy.

b) A Bunsen burner is designed to change _____ energy to _____ energy.　　　　　　　　　　　　　　[1]

c) A catapult which fires a pellet horizontally is designed to change _____ energy to _____ energy.　[1]

d) A microphone is designed to change _____ energy to _____ energy.　　　　　　　　　　　　　[1]

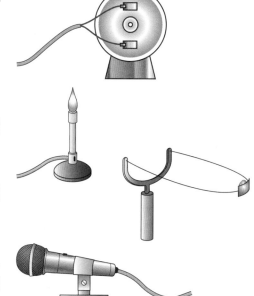

Answers

b) chemical energy to heat energy

c) strain energy to kinetic energy

d) sound energy to electrical energy

> **Exam tip**
>
> Why do you think it was necessary for the examiners to say that the pellet is fired horizontally in part c)? If the pellet was fired vertically, or at an angle upwards, strain PE would be converted to gravitational PE as well as kinetic energy. By firing the pellet horizontally, the examiners limit the acceptable response to strain PE and kinetic energy. In part d) the most common mistake involves confusion between microphones and loudspeakers. Microphones convert sound to electricity; loudspeakers convert electricity to sound.

Worked example 2

a) Explain what is meant by a renewable source of energy. **[1]**

b) In the table below tick (✓) the correct box to show whether the energy resource is renewable or non-renewable. **[4]**

Energy source	Renewable	Non-renewable
coal		
wind		
geothermal		
biomass		

c) Scientists working in Hawaii have discovered that there has been a big increase in the most important greenhouse gas over the past 50 years. Name the main greenhouse gas. How is most of this greenhouse gas produced? **[2]**

Scientists believe that an increase in the greenhouse effect will lead to a rise in temperature of the atmosphere.

d) What harm will this rise in temperature cause to the environment? **[1]**

Answers

a) A renewable resource is one that is replaced by nature in less than a human lifetime.

b)

Energy source	Renewable	Non-renewable
coal		✓
wind	✓	
geothermal	✓	
biomass	✓	

c) Carbon dioxide. It is produced when fossil fuels are burnt.

d) Global climate changes, with more frequent and more severe droughts, floods, hurricanes.

> **Exam tip**
>
> The common mistake made by GCSE students is to write that renewable resources 'can be used over and over again'. This is quite wrong. Once a unit of energy has been used by humans, that particular unit of energy can never be used again. That is why it is important to learn the correct definitions of renewable and non-renewable energy resources.

Work

Work is done when a force causes movement. The amount of work done is given by the formula:

> work done = force × distance moved in the direction of the force

or

> $W = F \times d$

Exam tip

This formula must be memorised.

Work, W, is measured in newton-metres (N m) or joules (J).

Force, F, is measured in newtons (N).

Distance, d, is measured in metres (m).

Worked example 3

1 A boat is rowed 50 m across a lake. Calculate the work done in joules if the average resistive force opposing the motion is 2500 N.   [3]

2 The work done by a pneumatic chisel in drilling to a depth of 20 cm is 1200 J. What is the average force exerted by the chisel?   [3]

Answers

1 Work done = 2500 N × 50 m = 125 000 J

2 Here there are two things to watch – the distance moved is given in centimetres, not metres, and you are required to find force, not work done. If your mathematical skills are weak, make the substitutions before doing any algebra.

Work done = force × distance

$$1200 = F \times 0.20$$

$$F = \frac{1200}{0.20}$$

$$F = 6000 \text{ N}$$

Exam tip

Always write the equation first, then make the substitutions.

Note the conversion to metres.

Occasionally, questions are asked to test what is meant by 'distance moved in the direction of the force'. Make sure you understand this.

Power

Power is the rate of doing work. Power is calculated using the formula:

> $$\text{power} = \frac{\text{work done}}{\text{time taken}}$$
>
> $$P = \frac{W}{t}$$

Exam tip

This formula must be memorised.

Power, P, is measured in joules per second (J/s) or watts (W).

Work, W, is measured in joules (J).

Time, t, is measured in seconds (s).

Worked example 4

1 To lift a girder through a height of 5 m a crane exerts an upward force of 12 000 N. The work is done in 30 seconds. Calculate the power of the crane. [4]

2 In a developing country a wind pump can raise 300 kg water through a vertical height of 8 m in 5 minutes. If 1 kg water weighs 10 N, calculate the useful work done and the output power of the pump. [3]

Answers

1 Work done = 12 000 × 5 = 60 000 J

$$\text{Power} = \frac{60\,000}{30} = 2000 \text{ W}$$

2 Force = 300 × 10 = 3000 N

Useful work = 3000 × 8 = 24 000 J

Time = 5 × 60 = 300 s

$$\text{Power output} = \frac{24\,000}{300} = 80 \text{ W}$$

> **Exam tip**
>
> This is a two-part question. First calculate the work done using $W = F \times d$, then find the power using $P = \frac{W}{t}$.

> **Exam tip**
>
> First use $W = F \times d$ to find the work done, remembering that the force is the total weight of the water. Then use $P = \frac{W}{t}$ to calculate the pump's power, but note that the time must be in seconds.

Measuring output power
Revised

Students taking GCSE Physics need to be able to describe experiments to measure the output power of both a student and an electric motor.

To measure your **personal power**, you need to find out how long it takes you to do a given amount of work.

First, find your weight in newtons. The easy way to do this is to find your mass in kilograms using bathroom scales, and then use the fact that 1 kg has a weight of 10 N. Then you need to find the height of a staircase. This can be done by measuring the average height of a riser (stair) and multiplying by the number of risers in the staircase. Finally, you need to have someone who will time you as you run up the stairs. Typical results are shown on the next page.

Measurements:

Mass of student in kg	45
Weight of student in N	450
Height of risers in cm	14.0, 13.8, 13.8, 14.0, 13.9
Average riser height in cm	13.9
Number of risers	30
Staircase height	$13.9 \times 30 = 417$ cm $= 4.17$ m
Time to run upstairs in s	5.2, 5.1, 4.9, 5.0, 4.8
Average time taken in s	5.0

Calculations:

Work = force × distance = $450 \times 4.17 = 1876.5$ J

$$\text{Power} = \frac{\text{work}}{\text{time}} = \frac{1876.5}{5.0} = 375 \text{ W (approx.)}$$

This figure of 375 W is typical of an average GCSE student. But note that the student could not keep up this power for more than a few seconds. In fact, the average adult has a sustained power of only about 75 W.

To measure the **output power of a motor** we measure the time, t, it takes for the motor to raise a known mass, m, through a known height, h, **at a constant speed**. Then the output power is given by the equation:

$$\text{output power} = \frac{\text{work}}{\text{time}} = \frac{mgh}{t}$$

where g is the gravitational field strength, 10 N/kg.

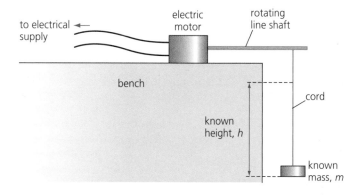

Comments on the validity and reliability of the data

	Comment
Reliability	The term reliability refers to the consistency with which we can confirm the result. In these experiments, the measured times are quite close, giving the user confidence in the reliability of the procedure.
Validity	The term validity refers to whether the experimental design allows us to measure the power of the pupil or motor. In the case of the motor experiment, the procedure is valid but the measured output power is only valid for the given input power and weight of the load.

Efficiency

Efficiency is defined by the formula:

$$\text{efficiency} = \frac{\text{useful energy output}}{\text{total energy input}}$$

Since efficiency is a ratio of useful energy output to total energy input, it has no unit. Another important thing to remember is that, since energy is wasted in every physical process, the efficiency of a machine is **always** less than 1.

> **Exam tip**
>
> Alternative definitions are possible involving work and power. Learn one and stick to it. A common mistake is to have the input on the top line and output on the bottom. This formula must be memorised.

Worked example 5

1   During a certain period of time the wind delivers 120 000 J of energy to the blades of a windmill and 30 000 J of electrical energy are produced. Find the efficiency of the windmill.   [3]

2   An electrical device uses 60 000 J of energy and has an efficiency of 0.4 (40%). What is the useful energy output?   [3]

Answers

1   Efficiency $= \dfrac{30\ 000}{120\ 000} = \dfrac{1}{4} = 0.25$

> **Exam tip**
>
> In questions about efficiency it is best to avoid the number given as a percentage (in this case, 40%) and instead use the decimal fraction (in this case 0.4).

2   $0.4 = \dfrac{\text{useful energy output}}{60\ 000}$

useful energy output $= 0.4 \times 60000 = 24\ 000$ J

Gravitational potential energy (GPE)

You are expected to remember that 1 kg has a weight of 10 N on Earth. This is just another way of saying that the gravitational field strength, g, on Earth is 10 N/kg. So the weight of an object, W, is given by:

$W = mg$

Remember that the value of g is different in different parts of the Universe. For example, g on the Moon is only about one-sixth of its value on Earth, so is approximately 1.6 N/kg.

When any object with mass is lifted, work is done on it against the force of gravity. The greater the mass of the object and the higher it is lifted, the more work has to be done. This work is then stored in the object as **gravitational potential energy** (**GPE**).

GPE = work done raising load mass (*m*) against the force of gravity (*g*)
through height (*h*)

= weight of mass *m* × height (*h*) = *mgh*

So

> GPE = *mgh*

Exam tip

This formula must be memorised.

m is the mass in kg.

g is the gravitational field strength in N/kg (10 N/kg on Earth).

h is the vertical height in m.

Worked example 6

a) How much work is done when the 4 kg mass falls 4.5 m? [3]

b) As the mass falls 4.5 m, the lamp produces 9 J of light energy.
Calculate the efficiency of this apparatus. [3]

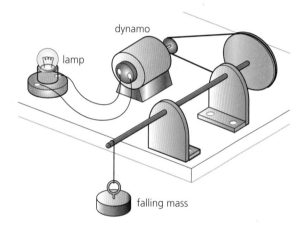

Answers

a) Work done = loss in gravitational potential
= energy of the mass
= *mgh*
= 4 × 10 × 4.5 = 180 J

b) Useful energy out = 9 J

$$\text{Efficiency} = \frac{9}{180} = \frac{1}{20} = 0.05$$

Kinetic energy

Revised

The kinetic energy of an object is the energy it has because it is moving. It
can be shown that an object's **kinetic energy (KE)** is given by the formula:

> KE = $\frac{1}{2}$ *mv*^{2}

Exam tip

This formula must be memorised.

m is the object's mass in kg.

v is the speed of the object in m/s.

Worked example 7

1 The combined mass of a speedboat and its driver is 300 kg. What is their total kinetic energy when travelling at 15 m/s? [3]

2 The kinetic energy of a pebble as it hits the water in a well is 10 J. If the speed of the pebble at that time is 25 m/s, calculate its mass. [4]

Answers

1 $KE = \frac{1}{2} mv^2$

$= \frac{1}{2} \times 300 \times (15)^2$

$= 33\ 750\ J$

Exam tip
Be careful: only the speed is squared.

2 This is a common type of question. To gain maximum marks you need to quote the formula, make the substitutions, carry out the necessary mathematics and then state the numerical answer with its unit.

$KE = \frac{1}{2} mv^2$

$10 = \frac{1}{2} \times m \times 25^2 = \frac{1}{2} \times m \times 625$

$10 = 312.5 \times m$

$m = \dfrac{10}{312.5} = 0.032\ kg$

Exam tip
Quote the formula for 1st mark.
Make the substitutions for 2nd mark.
Carry out arithmetic, giving answer and unit for the 3rd and 4th marks.

1 a) Kevin climbs a rope as shown in the diagram opposite.

   He climbs a vertical distance of 3.0 metres and he weighs 400 N.

   i) Calculate the work done by Kevin as he climbs the rope.

   ii) Kevin can develop a power of 200 W as he climbs the rope.

   Calculate how long it takes him to climb 3.0 metres up the rope.

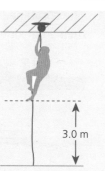

3.0 m

   b) A nail gun fires a nail of mass 5 g. The nail leaves the gun with a kinetic energy of 1 J.

   i) Calculate the velocity of the nail as it leaves the gun.

The nail gun is used to fix two pieces of wood together. The nail penetrates a distance of 0.005 m into the wood.

   ii) Calculate the average force opposing the nail as it penetrates into the wood.

2 A parcel is dropped from a stationary helicopter. The incomplete table below shows the kinetic energy, potential energy and total energy of the parcel at different points in the parcel's descent. The distance from A to B is **one third** of the distance from A to C.

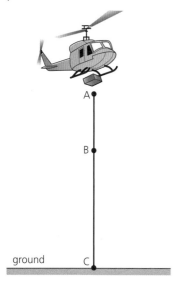

ground   C

Position of parcel	Potential energy in J	Kinetic energy in J	Total energy in J
highest point, A	3600	0	
at B		1200	
just before impact, C			3600

   a) Copy and complete the table. Ignore the effects of air resistance. **[3 marks]**

   b) The mass of the parcel is 20 kg. Calculate the height of the parcel at point A. Ignore the effects of air resistance. **[3 marks]**

3 a) An electric drill bores a hole 10 cm deep into a wall with an average force of 5000 N. Calculate the work done by the drill. **[3 marks]**

   b) The drill uses 8000 J of electrical energy in 10 seconds. Calculate the input power to the drill. **[3 marks]**

4 A crane is used to lift a load of 10 tonnes through a height of 3 metres (1 tonne = 1000 kg).

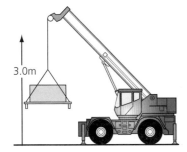

3.0m

a) Show that the weight of the load is 100 000 N. [1 mark]

b) State the equation connecting work done and force. [1 mark]

c) Calculate the work done in lifting the load. [2 marks]

d) The energy input to the crane while the load rises 3 m is 375 000 J. Calculate the efficiency of the crane. [3 marks]

e) State the equation which allows the output power of this crane to be calculated. [1 mark]

f) The crane takes 15 seconds to lift the load. Calculate the power **output** of the crane. [2 marks]

Exam tip

The mathematical requirements of both GCSE Physics and GCSE Double Award Science make it clear that you can only be asked to rearrange a formula at Higher Tier. Since the specification requires you to know and remember: work = force × distance, you know that you can only be asked to use this formula at Foundation Tier to calculate work (not force or distance). At Higher Tier you could be asked to use the formula to find work, force or distance.

Go online for the answers ————————————————————— Online

5 Moments

Centre of gravity

Revised

The centre of gravity (centre of mass) of an object is the point through which the entire weight of that object may be considered to act.

Exam tip
This definition must be memorised.

Only for regularly-shaped objects is the centre of mass, G, at the centre of the object. Centre of mass is often wrongly thought of as the point where the object would balance. The centre of mass of a Polo® mint, for example, is at the centre of the mint – but it would certainly not balance there!

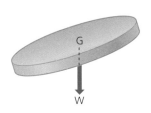
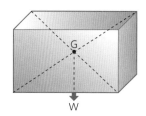

Moment of a force

Revised

Opening a door, cutting with scissors and using a nutcracker are all examples of the application of **moments** or **turning forces**. So what is a moment?

The moment of a force about a pivot is the product of the force and the perpendicular distance from the force to the pivot.

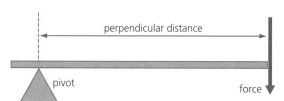

Moments have a direction – they are either clockwise or anticlockwise.

moment of a force (N cm) = force (N) × perpendicular distance from
the pivot (cm)

The behaviour of levers is summed up in a law known as the **Principle of Moments**. This law states:

When a lever is balanced, the sum of the clockwise moments about any point equals the sum of the anticlockwise moments about the same point.

Exam tip
This law must be memorised.

When an object is balanced at a pivot other than at its centre of gravity, its weight will provide a moment or turning effect.

You need to be able to describe the experimental work necessary to show the Principle of Moments.

Equilibrium and stability

A body is in equilibrium when both the resultant force and resultant turning effect on it are zero. There are three types of equilibrium, which are determined by what happens to the object when it is given a small push.

A ball on a flat piece of ground is in **neutral equilibrium**. When it is given a gentle push the ball rolls, keeping its centre of gravity at the same height above the point of contact with the ground.

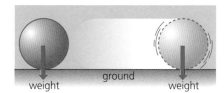

A pencil balanced on its point is in **unstable equilibrium**. It is balanced with its centre of gravity above its base, but a small push will move its centre of gravity downwards, creating an unbalanced moment about the point and causing the pencil to topple, as shown in the right hand diagram.

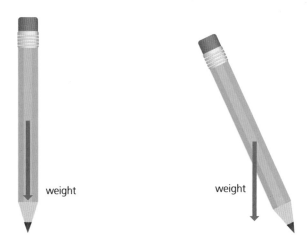

A car on a road is in **stable equilibrium**. Look at the diagrams on the next page. If the car is tilted (b), the centre of gravity is lifted. In this position, the action of the weight keeps the car on the road. In (c) the centre of gravity lies above the wheels, so the car is in a position of unstable equilibrium. If the car tips further (d), the weight acts outside the wheel base and provides a turning effect to turn the car over. Cars with a low centre of gravity and a wide wheelbase are the most stable on the road.

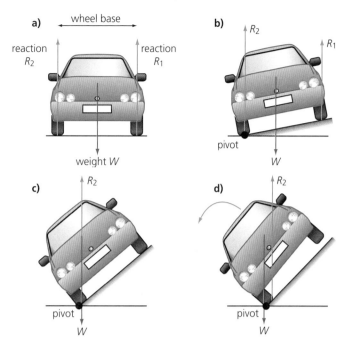

For **maximum stability** we want:

● a base that is as wide as possible, and

● a **centre of gravity** that is as **low** as possible.

Worked example 1

1 A body-builder lifts a weight of 4000 N suspended from a long metal bar.

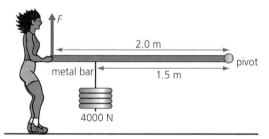

a) Calculate the moment created by the 4000 N about the pivot. [3]

b) The body-builder exerts a force *F* to lift the weight off the floor. Use the Principle of Moments to find the force *F*. [3]

c) Use the answer to part **b)** to calculate the size and direction of the force acting through the pivot. What assumption have you made? [3]

2 A uniform trap door of mass 4 kg is held in place by a long hinge on one side and a catch on the opposite side. The catch provides an upward vertical force *F*. The weight of the trap door acts through point G, which is 25 cm from the hinge and 25 cm from the catch.

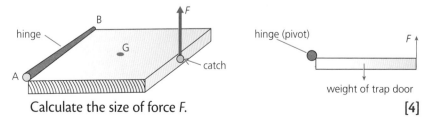

Calculate the size of force *F*. [4]

Answers

1 a) Moment = force × distance to pivot = 4000 N × 1.5 m
= 6000 Nm anticlockwise

b) By the Principle of Moments,
anticlockwise moments = clockwise moments
So, 6000 = F × distance to pivot = F × 2
Hence, F = 3000 N

c) There is a 4000 N downward force and a 3000 N upward force on the lever.
The upward forces must balance the downward forces on the bar, so there must also be a force of 1000 N upwards at the pivot, otherwise the bar will move downwards. The upward force at the pivot does not produce a moment.
The assumption made is that the bar itself is of negligible weight.

2 Weight of trap door = mg = 4 × 10 = 40 N.
It acts vertically down through G.

By the Principle of Moments,
anticlockwise moments = clockwise moments about AB
$F × 50 = 40 × 25 = 1000$, so $F = \dfrac{1000}{50} = 20$ N

Exam tip

Lever questions can be challenging and you must get practice doing them. Try as many revision and examination questions as you can.

Revision Questions

Tested

1 A large steel beam weighs 20 kN. A crane is used to raise this large steel beam into a vertical position, pivoting it about one end. The crane exerts a force F to just lift the end A of the beam off the ground. The length of the beam is 5 m. This arrangement is shown in the diagram below.

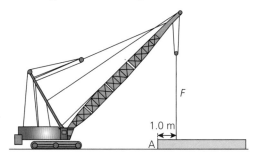

a) The beam can be treated as a lever. Mark clearly with the letter P the pivot. **[1 mark]**

b) Copy the diagram above and draw an arrow to show where and in what direction the weight of the beam acts. Assume the beam is of uniform width. **[2 marks]**

c) By applying the Principle of Moments, calculate the size of the upward force F that the crane must exert to just raise end A of the beam off the ground. **[4 marks]**

2 A wheelbarrow loaded with sand is being wheeled along a level road. The weight of the wheelbarrow and the sand in it is 1500 N.

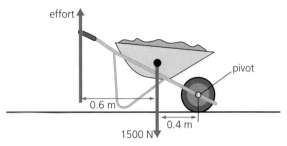

a) Calculate the moment of the 1500 N force about the pivot. [4 marks]

b) Calculate the size of the effort at the handles. [3 marks]

c) What force acts at the pivot? [2 marks]

3 A force of 600 N just raises the jockey wheel of a caravan off the ground, in order to attach the caravan to a car. See the diagram below. Calculate the weight of the caravan. [3 marks]

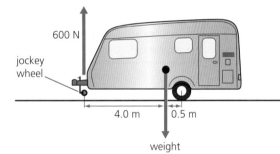

> **Exam tip**
> Identify the pivot and take care with distances.

4 a) School caretakers often use trucks such as the one shown below to move heavy objects around. The design of the truck makes it easier to lift the load and the wheels make it easy to move the load from one place to another.

   i) Copy the diagram and mark and label the position of the pivot. You should also mark the load force and the effort force needed to lift the load. Show clearly where they act and the direction in which they act. [5 marks]

   ii) Explain, using the idea of moments, why the design of the truck makes it easier to lift the load. [2 marks]

b) i) The diagram shows a solid rectangular block. The block is tilted to the position shown. When it is released, will it return to stand upright again or will it topple over? Explain your answer. **[3 marks]**

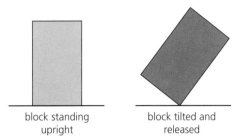

block standing upright   block tilted and released

ii) To find the weight of a metre ruler Susan set up the apparatus shown below. The metre rule is pivoted at the 30 cm mark and a weight of 2.5 N is moved along the metre rule until the ruler is balanced. Using the information shown, calculate the weight of the metre ruler. **[4 marks]**

18 cm

2.5 N

5 A simplified diagram of a tower crane is shown below. It is holding a load of 5000 N.

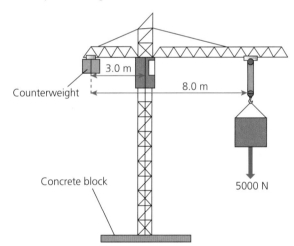

Counterweight

3.0 m

8.0 m

Concrete block

5000 N

a) Calculate the force provided by the counterweight when the load is in the position shown. **[4 marks]**

b) For stability the tower crane is bolted to a large concrete block. If the total downward force on the block is 30 000 N, calculate the weight of the crane. **[4 marks]**

> **Exam tip**
>
> When answering questions on the Principle of Moments, always write ACWM = CWM, and then it is useful to write $F_1d_1 = F_2d_2$. After that find the forces involved and the distances from the pivot, substitute and solve the equation. Easy!

Go online for the answers ━━━━━━━━━━━━━━━━━━━━━━━━━━ Online

6 Waves

Waves transfer energy from one point to another but they do not transfer matter. Waves are produced as a result of **vibrations** and can be classified as **longitudinal** or **transverse** depending on how the particles of matter vibrate.

Longitudinal waves

A **longitudinal wave** is one in which the particles vibrate **parallel** to the direction in which the wave is travelling. Some examples of longitudinal waves are:

● sound waves

● some slinky spring waves.

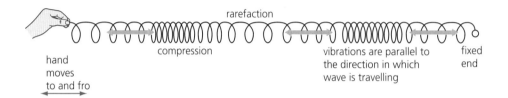

You can demonstrate longitudinal waves by moving your hand back and forth parallel to the axis of a stretched slinky spring. **Compressions** are places where the coils or particles bunch together. **Rarefactions** are places where the coils or particles are furthest apart. These move along the spring.

All longitudinal waves are made up of compressions and rarefactions. In sound waves, the particles are the molecules of the material through which the sound is travelling. These molecules bunch together and separate, much as they do in a longitudinal wave on a slinky spring.

Transverse waves

A **transverse wave** is one in which the particles vibrate **at 90°** to the direction in which the wave is travelling. Most waves in nature are transverse. Some examples of transverse waves are:

● water waves

● some slinky spring waves

● waves on strings and ropes

● electromagnetic waves.

We can demonstrate a transverse wave using a slinky spring as shown in the diagram below. Notice that the hand moves up and down at 90° to the axis of the spring. The movement of the string tied to one of the coils shows how the particles are moving.

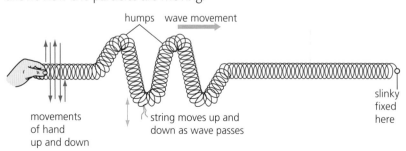

Frequency, wavelength and amplitude of transverse waves

Revised ☐

There are a number of important definitions relating to waves that must be learned.

The **frequency** of a wave is the number of complete waves passing a fixed point in 1 second. Frequency is given the symbol f, and is measured in units called **hertz** (abbreviation Hz).

The **wavelength of a transverse wave** is the distance between two consecutive crests or troughs. Wavelength is given the symbol λ, and is measured in metres. λ is the Greek letter 'l' and is pronounced *lambda*.

The **amplitude** of a wave is the greatest displacement of the wave from its undisturbed position. Amplitude is measured in metres.

The diagram below illustrates the wavelength and amplitude of a transverse wave in water.

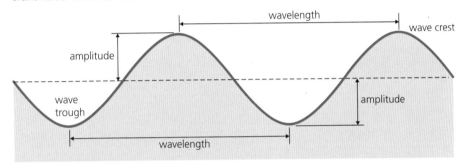

Frequency, wavelength and amplitude of longitudinal waves

Revised ☐

For a longitudinal wave, it helps to use slightly different definitions.

The **frequency** is the number of vibrations made by a particle in 1 second. (In the diagram below right, 1 vibration = A-B-A.)

The **wavelength of a longitudinal wave** is the distance between the centre of one compression (or rarefaction) and the next.

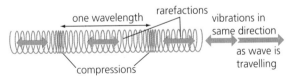

The **amplitude** is the maximum distance any particle in the wave moves from the centre (equilibrium position) of its motion.

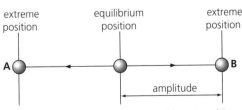

particle vibrates between positions A and B

The wave equation

Imagine a wave with wavelength λ (metres) and frequency f (hertz).

From the definition of frequency, in 1 second f waves pass a fixed point. Each wave has a length λ.

So, the total distance travelled every second is $f \times λ$.

But the distance travelled in 1 second is the speed. So:

> speed of wave = frequency × wavelength
> $$v = f \times λ$$

Exam tip

This is known as the wave equation and it must be memorised.

where:

v = speed of the waves

f = frequency in Hz

λ = wavelength

Note that the units used in the wave equation must be consistent, as shown in the table below.

Frequency	Wavelength	Speed
always in hertz	cm	cm/s
	m	m/s
	km	km/s

Worked example 1

As a wave passes through a certain medium, the particles vibrate through a distance of 5 cm, parallel to the direction of the wave, as shown in the diagram below.

direction of travel of the wave

 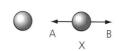

particle X vibrates from A to B and back again

In the diagram, the particle marked X vibrates through a distance of 5 cm (AB = 5 cm).

a) What kind of wave is this? [1]

b) What is the amplitude of the wave? [1]

The time for one complete vibration of the particles of the medium is 0.5 seconds.

c) Calculate the frequency of the wave. [2]

d) The wavelength of the wave is 50 cm. Calculate its speed. [2]

Exam tip

- In this type of question many candidates wrongly think that the amplitude is the distance AB (5 cm in this case).

- To gain credit for part **d)**, you have to use $v = fλ$, so it is very important to write *some* number for the frequency in part c) and then carry that number forward to find the wave speed. *Never* leave an answer line blank in a numerical question!

Exam tip

Make certain you understand the terms transverse, longitudinal, amplitude, wavelength and frequency and can use the wave equation. These topics come up almost every year!

Answers

a) Longitudinal

b) 2.5 cm

c) 1 vibration in 0.5 s = 2 vibrations/second, so f = 2 Hz

d) $v = fλ = 2 \times 50 = 100$ cm/s

Plane wavefronts

Much can be learned about the behaviour of waves from a ripple tank. A motor makes a straight edge dipping into a tank of water produce straight water waves known as plane waves. These plane waves can be used to study **reflection** and **refraction**. A hand-held stroboscope can be used to 'freeze the motion' so that wavelength measurements can be made.

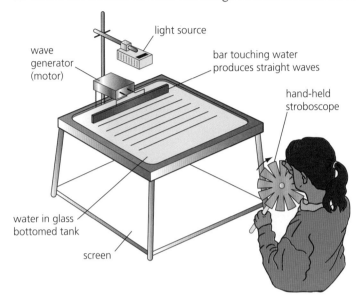

Wave reflection

The reflecting barrier in the ripple tank must be big enough to prevent the water waves going 'over the top'.

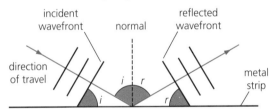

Note that:

● the angle of incidence is always equal to the angle of reflection

● the wavelengths of the incident and reflected waves are equal

● there is continuity of the incident and reflected waves at the barrier

● the frequencies of the incident and reflected waves are equal

● the speeds of the incident and reflected waves are equal

● the angle between a wavefront and the direction of travel is always 90°.

Wave refraction

In the diagram below waves are travelling from deep water to shallow water. A region of shallow water in a ripple tank can be made by immersing a rectangular glass block. The water directly above the sunken glass is shallow while the surrounding water is deeper.

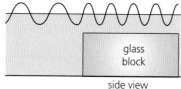

side view

Ripple tank studies show that when waves travel from deep water into shallow water:

- the waves slow down
- the **wavelength** of the waves **decreases**
- the frequency of the waves is unchanged.

If the waves enter the shallow region obliquely (at an angle), the angle of incidence in the deep water is always greater than the angle of refraction in the shallow water, as shown below. Note carefully the **continuity** of the waves from deep to shallow water.

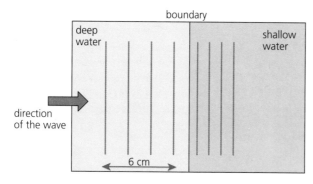

refracted wavefronts in shallow water

incident wavefronts in deep water

Worked example 2

The diagram shows what happens when a water wave moves from deep water to shallow water. The diagram is not full scale.

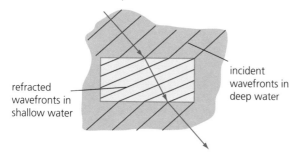

boundary

deep water

shallow water

direction of the wave

6 cm

Exam tip

GCSE examiners frequently ask questions that require students to draw or complete wave diagrams.

a) What is the wavelength of the water wave in deep water? [2]

The water wave is made by a long bar vibrating in the water.

b) The long bar makes 20 vibrations in 5 seconds. Calculate the frequency of the water wave produced. [2]

c) Using your answers to parts a) and b) calculate the speed of the water wave in the deep water. [3]

The direction of the boundary is now changed so that the water wave enters the shallow water at an angle as shown in the diagram below.

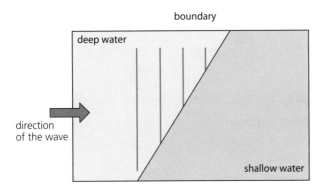

boundary

deep water

direction of the wave

shallow water

d) Complete the diagram above to show what happens to the water wave in the shallow water. [5]
e) State what causes this change of direction. [1]

Answers

a) $3\lambda = 6\,cm$, so $\lambda = 2\,cm$

b) $f = \dfrac{20}{5} = 4\,Hz$

c) $v = f\lambda = 4 \times 2 = 8\,cm/s$

d) See diagram below – observe that: the incident and refracted wavefronts are continuous; the bending is in the correct direction to produce waves of smaller wavelength; the refracted wavefronts are parallel to each other and equally spaced.

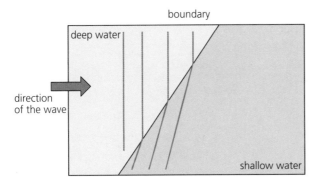

boundary

deep water

direction of the wave

shallow water

e) Waves slow down when they enter shallower water. This causes them to change direction.

> **Exam tip**
> Remember, there is never a change in frequency when waves reflect or refract. There is always a change in wavelength when waves refract, but never when they reflect.

Water wave–light analogy

The analogy between the reflection and refraction of water waves and the reflection and refraction of light is discussed on page 58.

Sound waves are produced when an object vibrates at a frequency that the ear can detect. The range of human hearing is from around 20 Hz to 20 000 Hz (20 kHz), although the upper limit decreases with age. Sound of frequencies above 20 kHz cannot be heard by humans and is called **ultrasound**. Ultrasound can be heard by bats, dogs and some other animals.

Sound travels through materials as a longitudinal wave as energy passes from molecule to molecule. The **sound energy passes from particle to particle**, which explains why sound cannot travel through a vacuum, where there are no particles.

When sound waves hit a hard surface, they **reflect**. A reflection of sound, ultrasound, microwaves or radio waves is called **an echo**.

Sonar and radar

Sonar is an acronym for **so**und **na**vigation and **r**anging. Radar is an acronym for **ra**dio **d**etection **a**nd **r**anging. Both processes use echoes to locate a target and measure how far away it is.

Sonar uses ultrasound, which travels at about 340 m/s in air and at about 1500 m/s in water. Sonar is used to measure distances, from the size of a baby's head in the womb (several cm) to the depth of a submarine below the surface (several km). Sonar is also limited to fairly slow-moving objects, like the opening and closing of the valves within the heart.

Radar uses electromagnetic waves of wavelengths ranging from about 3 cm to a few metres. This is around the area where the microwave region of the electromagnetic spectrum ends and the radio region begins. Because **radar waves travel so quickly** (about 300 000 km/s in air) and are not absorbed significantly by the air, they are used to locate very distant objects that may be moving very rapidly, such as tracking a spacecraft as it leaves the Earth's atmosphere.

Applications of the echo principle

Sonar uses ultrasound to detect objects under water.

Worked example 3

1   A pulse of ultrasound is emitted upwards by a submarine deep below the ice sheet in the Arctic Ocean, as shown here.

Some time later the submarine detects an echo, and a short time after that it detects a second echo.

a) Explain why two echoes are produced in this case. [2]

b) To measure the distance to the ocean floor the submarine emits a pulse of ultrasound downwards. The echo of this pulse is detected 0.4 s after it was emitted. [4]
The speed of ultrasound in water is 1500 m/s.
Use the equation: distance = speed × time to help you calculate the distance from the submarine to the floor of the ocean.

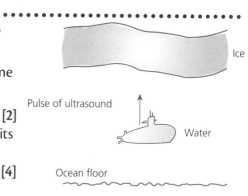

Ice

Pulse of ultrasound

Water

Ocean floor

2 A ship sends out a pulse of ultrasound, which is reflected from the seabed 675 m below the ship. In seawater ultrasound travels at 1500 m/s. Calculate how long it takes for the ultrasound to travel from the ship to the seabed and back to the ship. **[4]**

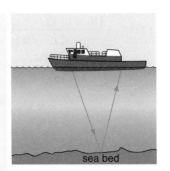
sea bed

3 An aircraft is flying at a distance of 12 000 m from an air-traffic control tower. A radar pulse is emitted from the top of the tower. Radar travels at 3×10^8 m/s in air.

> **Exam tip**
>
> Questions on echoes are a great favourite with examiners and are really easy when you know how to do them!

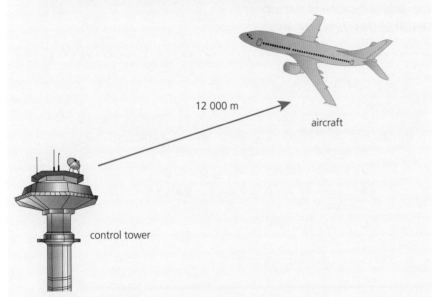
12 000 m
aircraft
control tower

a) How long after the radar pulse is emitted is it before the echo is detected at the tower? **[4]**

b) Why is ultrasound not suitable to detect such aircraft? **[2]**

Answers

1 a) The first echo is the reflection from the water–ice boundary.
The second echo is the reflection from the ice–air boundary.

b) Distance to ocean floor and back to submarine
= speed of ultrasound × time taken for ultrasound to travel to ocean floor and back
= 1500 × 0.4 = 600 m
So distance to ocean floor = ½ × 600 = 300 m.

2 Time taken = $\dfrac{\text{total distance travelled}}{\text{speed of ultrasound}}$

$= \dfrac{(2 \times 675)}{1500}$

$= \dfrac{1350}{1500} = 0.9\,\text{s}$

Note: This question is Higher Tier because you are asked to find the time, not the distance.

> **Exam tip**
>
> ● A common mistake is forgetting to halve the final distance.
>
> ● The equation:
> distance = speed × time was given to avoid the need for Foundation students to carry out algebra. In Higher Tier papers this formula would not be supplied

3 a) Time taken $= \dfrac{\text{total distance travelled}}{\text{speed of ultrasound}}$

$= \dfrac{(2 \times 12\,000)}{3 \times 10^8}$

$= \dfrac{24\,000}{3 \times 10^8} = 8 \times 10^{-5}\,\text{s}$

$= 80\,\mu\text{s}$

b) The speed of ultrasound is so slow compared to radar waves that by the time the ultrasound reached the original location of the aircraft, (about 35 s) it would have moved much further away.

Applications of ultrasound

In industry	In medicine
● Scanning metal casings for faults or cracks	● Removing harmful tartar from teeth
● Mapping the ocean floor in oceanography	● Scanning soft tissues to diagnose cancers
● Fish location by sea-going trawlers	● Scanning a womb to check the development of the unborn child
● Cleaning sensitive electronic equipment	● Breaking up kidney stones

Revision Questions

Tested

1 A stretched slinky spring rests on a table. Waves can be set up on the slinky spring so that the wave profile (shape) will travel from end A to end B.

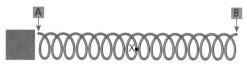

a) In the box at end A, draw an arrow to show the direction of the energy flow due to the wave. [1 mark]

b) Describe how point X will move when a **longitudinal** wave passes along the slinky. [2 marks]

c) Describe the motion of the particles in a **transverse** wave. [1 mark]

d) Give an example of a transverse wave, other than those generated on a slinky spring. [1 mark]

2 Sarah generates water waves in a ripple tank.

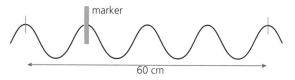

a) What is the wavelength of the water waves? [1 mark]

Sarah observes 10 waves passing a marker in 4 seconds.

b) How many waves pass the marker in 1 second? [1 mark]

c) Use your answer to **b)** to state the frequency of the water waves. [2 marks]

d) Calculate the speed of the water waves. [3 marks]

3 Chris uses the apparatus shown below to produce and detect sound waves.

Cathode
ray oscilloscope
(CRO)

loudspeaker

microphone

He makes three changes to the sound produced. The table below shows the initial CRO trace before the change is made and the final CRO trace after the change is made. Copy and complete the table.

	Initial CRO trace	Final CRO trace	Changes in the CRO trace	Change in sound heard by Chris
a)				loudness decreases
b)			frequency increases	
c)			wave shape changes	

[3 marks]

Go online for the answers   Online

7 Light

Electromagnetic waves

These are seven members of a family of waves known collectively as the **electromagnetic spectrum**. They all:

- can travel in a **vacuum** – this property is unique to electromagnetic waves
- travel at exactly the **same speed** in a vacuum
- are **transverse** waves.

You need to remember the names of the members of the electromagnetic spectrum in order of increasing wavelength, together with their uses and dangers.

> **Exam tip**
>
> Questions on the uses and dangers of electromagnetic waves come up very often. They are easy when you know the table below. So learn it thoroughly!

Electromagnetic wave	Typical wavelength	Uses	Dangers
Gamma (γ) waves	0.01 nm	• Can destroy viruses, fungi, bacteria and living cells • Used to kill cancer cells, sterilise medical equipment and kill bacteria and fungi on food	• Can disrupt DNA and cause cancers
X-rays	0.1 nm	• Used in medicine for diagnosis (detecting broken bones or body scanning to detect tumours) and to kill cancer cells	• Can disrupt DNA and cause cancers
Ultraviolet light	10 nm	• Used to give a sun-tan • Used to detect bank-note forgeries • Kills bacteria in water chillers	• Can cause skin cancer
Visible light	0.5 μm	• Used for human vision, photography and photosynthesis	• Can cause snow-blindness
Infrared light	0.01 mm	• Used in toasters, ovens, grills and stoves • Used in night-vision goggles and by scientists to photograph nocturnal animals • Used in guided weapons and TV remote controls	• Damages cells by burning
Microwaves	3 cm	• Used in mobile phones and for fast food preparation	• Can cause eye cataracts
Radio waves	1000 m	• Used extensively for communication for entertainment and by the emergency services (police, fire and ambulance)	• No known dangers

Health risks associated with mobile phones and communication masts

Mobile phones work by dividing a country into areas (called cells), each about 10–15 km wide. Each cell has its own microwave transmitter and receiver. When a call is made, rapid computer switching passes the call from one cell to another until it finally reaches the cell where the phone being called is to be found. The presence of so many microwave masts for mobile phones throughout the country has caused some people to link mobile phones with cancer. Others claim that because mobile phones use microwaves, holding the phone close to your ear can cause the brain to be damaged.

To investigate these claims, a committee known as the Independent Expert Group on Mobile Phones, chaired by Sir William Stewart FRS, was asked by the British Government to investigate and make recommendations. This high-powered group of experts reported that there is no *proven* case of damage being done to people either by communication masts or mobile phones. The full report is available on the internet at http://www.iegmp.org.uk/report/text.htm.

The Stewart report was published in April 2000. Since then expert groups in other European countries and in the USA have recommended the **precautionary principle** is followed: even if the chances of negative health effects are low, it makes sense to avoid unnecessary risk. This means:

- **Children** under the age of nine should **use mobile phones very sparingly,** because their small body mass would make any possible harm to them more severe.

- People should be encouraged to **use mobile phones with headsets** or speaker-phones whenever possible, so as to keep their heads as far as possible from the radiation-emitting handset.

- Mobile phone masts should **not be erected close to schools** or hospitals.

Light

Revised

Objects that produce light are **luminous**. We see such objects because light travels from them directly to our eyes. We see non-luminous objects only when they scatter (reflect) light from luminous objects into our eyes. The Sun, stars and candle flames are examples of luminous objects. The Earth, the Moon, the planets and school textbooks are examples of non-luminous objects.

Materials such as air, glass and water through which light travels readily are **transparent**. If light cannot travel through a material we call it **opaque**.

Reflection of light

Revised

The light ray striking the mirror is called the incident ray. The normal is the imaginary line that meets the mirror at right angles at the point of incidence. The light ray travelling away from the mirror is called the reflected ray.

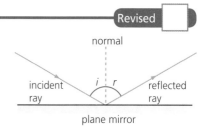

Experiments show that when light is reflected **the angle of incidence (i) is always equal to the angle of reflection (r)**. This is known as the **Law of Reflection**.

Note that a ray of light striking the mirror at 90° is reflected back along its original path. In this case the angles of incidence and reflection are both 0°.

You should be able to describe an experiment to demonstrate this law, as shown on the next page.

Proving the law of reflection

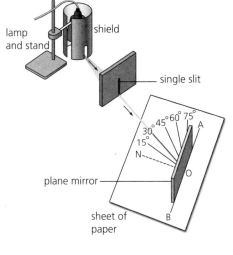

1 With a sharp pencil and a ruler, draw a straight line AOB on a sheet of white paper using a ruler.

2 Use a protractor to draw a normal, N, at point O.

3 With the protractor, draw straight lines at various angles to the normal ranging from 15° to 75°.

4 Place a plane mirror on the paper so that its back rests on the line AOB.

5 Using a ray box, shine a ray of light along the line marked 15°.

6 Mark two crosses on the reflected ray on the paper.

7 Remove the mirror, use a ruler to join the crosses on the paper with a pencil, and extend the line backwards to point O – this line shows the reflected ray.

8 Measure the angle of reflection with a protractor.

9 Record in a table the angles of incidence and reflection.

10 Repeat the experiment for different angles of incidence up to 75°.

The image in a plane mirror

You should be able to describe an experiment to investigate the properties of the image in a plane mirror by **ray tracing**.

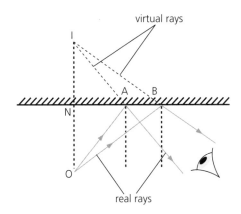

1 Support a plane mirror vertically on a sheet of white paper, and with a pencil draw a straight line at the back to mark the position of the reflecting surface.

2 Use a ray box to direct two rays of light from point O towards points A and B on the mirror.

3 Mark the position of point O with a cross using a pencil.

4 Mark two crosses on each of the real reflected rays.

5 Remove both the ray box and the mirror.

6 Using a ruler, join the crosses with a pencil line so as to obtain the paths of the real rays from A and B.

7 Extend these lines behind the mirror (these are called virtual rays) – they meet at I, the point where the image was formed.

8 Measure the distance from the image I to the mirror line (IN) and the distance from the object O to the mirror line (ON) – they should be the same.

9 Repeat the experiment for different positions of the object O.

10 In each case, the object O and its image I should be the same perpendicular distance from the mirror.

Summary

The image in a plane mirror is:

- virtual
- the same size as the object
- laterally inverted
- the same distance behind the mirror as the object is in front.

The diagram below shows what happens when light from an object strikes a plane (flat) mirror. The reflected rays get further apart (diverge) and enter the eye. But the eye follows the rays back in a straight line. The rays entering the eye all appear to come from the same point behind the mirror (image). A mirror image like this is not caused by rays of light coming to a focus, and is called a **virtual** image. Virtual images cannot be projected on to a screen. Images that can be projected on to a screen are called **real** images.

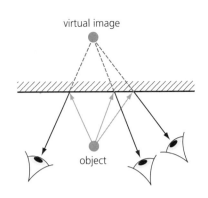

Worked example 1

1   This question is about the reflection of light.

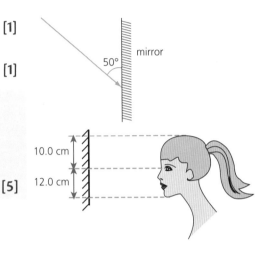

   a) Draw the appropriate normal on the diagram opposite.   [1]

   b) What is the angle of reflection for the diagram opposite?   [1]

2   Jane stands in front of a plane mirror as shown.

   By drawing appropriate rays on the diagram, determine the shortest length of mirror needed to allow Jane to see all of her face, i.e. from the top of her head to the bottom of her chin.   [5]

Answers

1   a) Line drawn perpendicular to mirror at point of incidence.

   b) 40°

2   Ray from top of head (where dotted line touches head) to point on mirror midway between upper two dotted lines and reflected ray into Jane's eye. Ray from Jane's chin (where dotted line touches chin) to point on mirror midway between lower two dotted lines and reflected ray into Jane's eye.
   Shortest length of mirror is 5 + 6 = 11 cm

Exam tip

Make sure you can describe the experiment to prove the law of reflection of light and apply the law to solve problems like these.

Refraction of light ————————————————— Revised ☐

Refraction is the change in the direction of a beam of light as it travels from one material into another. It occurs because light travels at different speeds in different materials.

Material	Speed of light in m/s
Air	300 000 000
Water	225 000 000
Glass	200 000 000

In every case where refraction occurs, some light is reflected internally. In the diagram opposite, observe carefully the **direction** in which the light bends on refraction.

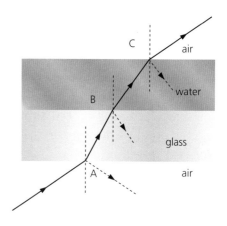

- When **light slows down**, it bends **towards the normal.**
- When **light speeds up**, it bends **away from the normal**.

Note that a ray of light striking a boundary at 90° passes through without bending. In this case the angles of incidence and refraction are both 0°.

There is no need to remember the figures for the speed of light in various materials, but you do need to know that **light travels faster in air** than in any other material. You also need to be able to describe an experiment to measure the angles of incidence and refraction by ray tracing.

Measuring the angles of incidence and refraction

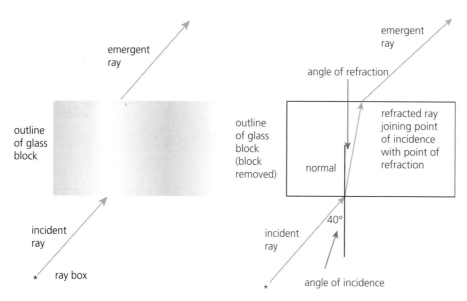

- Place the glass block on a sheet of white paper and draw around its outline with a sharp pencil.
- Remove the block and draw a normal near the middle of one of the longer sides of the block.
- Use a protractor to draw a line representing an incident ray at an angle of incidence i of 40°.
- Replace the block on its outline on the paper.
- Place the ray box to direct a ray of light along the line drawn.
- Mark the path of the emergent ray.
- Remove the block and join the points of incidence and emergence with a straight line to construct the path of the ray through the block.
- Repeat this procedure for angles of incidence i of 50°, 60° and 70° using the same normal line.
- Use your diagram to make measurements of the angles of refraction r on entry into the block and record the angles of refraction in a table like the one below.

Angle of incidence, i, in degrees	40	50	60	70
Angle of refraction, r, in degrees	25	31	35	39

↑ **Typical results for a refraction experiment with a glass block.**

Dispersion

Dispersion is the breaking up of white light into its component colours. Each colour in white light travels at the same speed in air, but at a slightly different speed in glass. This means that each colour bends by a slightly different amount when it refracts:

● **Red light is fastest in glass**, so it refracts (bends) the least.
● **Violet light is slowest in glass** and refracts the most.

The separated colours are called the **visible spectrum**.

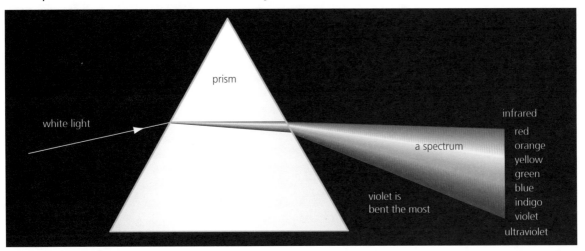

Total internal reflection

● When light travels from glass into air it bends away from the normal towards the glass. At the same time a weak internally reflected ray is observed.

● As the angle of incidence in glass increases, the refracted ray becomes weaker and the internally reflected ray becomes stronger, until a very weak refracted ray is observed with a large angle of refraction.

● The angle of incidence in glass that results in an angle of refraction in air of 90° is called the **critical angle, c**. The critical angle for glass is typically around 42°.

● At angles of incidence above the critical angle there is no refraction – the light is totally internally reflected.

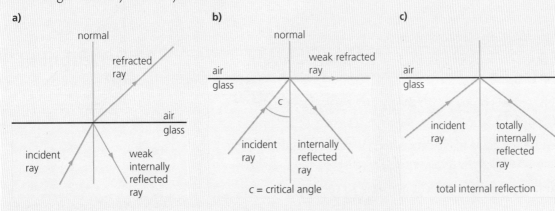

Note: GCSE Higher Physics students need to be able to describe the experiment that follows, to investigate the critical angle in a semi-circular glass block.

Measuring the critical angle

- Place a semi-circular glass block on a sheet of white paper and draw around its outline with a sharp pencil.
- Direct a ray of light from a ray box towards the centre of a semi-circular glass block as shown in Diagram 1.
- Observe that there is no refraction at the curved surface of the block. This is because the ray is incident normally at the glass.
- The light refracts at the straight edge of the block and a weak internally reflected ray is also observed.

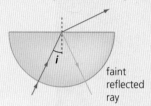

faint reflected ray

↑ **Diagram 1**

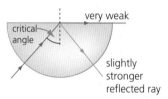

very weak

critical angle

slightly stronger reflected ray

↑ **Diagram 2**

- Move the ray-box to the left so as to increase the angle of incidence at the straight edge of the block.
- Continue moving the ray-box to the left until the refracted ray emerges along the straight edge of the block as in Diagram 2.
- Observe that the refracted ray is now very weak and the internally reflected ray is now stronger.
- Mark with a pencil two points on the incident ray as far apart as possible.
- Confirm that if the angle of incidence is now increased, the refracted ray vanishes and all the light is internally reflected within the glass block, as in Diagram 3.
- Remove the glass block and use a ruler to join the points to show the path of the incident ray to the straight edge of the block as in Diagram 2.
- Use a protractor to draw the normal at the straight edge and measure the critical angle.

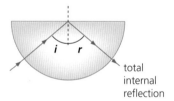

i r

total internal reflection

↑ **Diagram 3**

Critical angle and total internal reflection in prisms

- The critical angle for glass is approximately 42°.
- Consider the passage of a ray of light through an isosceles right-angled glass prism as in Diagram 4.
- At the first surface the light ray strikes the glass normally (at 90°) so there is no refraction.
- At the hypotenuse the angle of incidence is 45°, which is greater than the critical angle, so the light is totally internally reflected through 90°.
- At the third surface the light is incident normally, so there is no refraction.

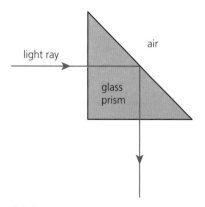

light ray

air

glass prism

↑ **Diagram 4**

- Diagram 5 shows how two 90° isosceles prisms can be used to make a periscope of the type used in submarines.
    - Cheaper and less effective periscopes use mirrors instead of prisms.
    - Note that the total internal reflection always occurs at the hypotenuse.
- Diagram 6 shows how a single 90° isosceles prism can be used to turn a ray of light through 180°.
    - This is used in red reflectors on the backs of cars and bicycles.
- Diagram 7 shows how two 90° isosceles prisms can be used to turn a ray of light through 180°.
    - The air gap between the prisms can be several cm long.
    - This is used in binoculars to give a similar effect to that of a telescope, but in a shorter device.

Total internal reflection is used in:
- binoculars
- periscopes
- optical fibres
- endoscopes.

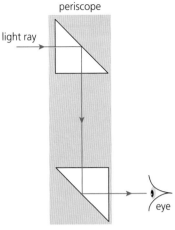

↑ Diagram 5

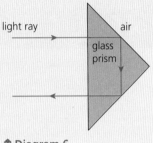

↑ Diagram 6

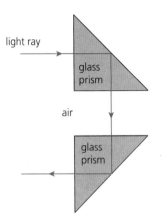

↑ Diagram 7

Optical fibres

Optical fibres are used in telecommunications and endoscopy.

- They are lengths of solid glass (inner core) with an outer glass cladding and a protective plastic sheath.
- Provided that the fibre is not bent too tightly, light will strike the core–cladding boundary at an angle greater than the critical angle and will be totally internally reflected at the surface of the glass core.
- However, every optical fibre has some imperfections at its reflecting surface and this means that the signal must be boosted every kilometre or so in communications links.
- Optical fibres are used to transmit both telephone and video signals over long distances.
- The big advantage of optical fibres is that they can carry much, much more information than a copper cable of the same diameter.
- What happens if the optical fibre is too tightly bent? If this happens, the angle of incidence at the core–cladding boundary may become less than the critical angle and light will be lost by refraction into the cladding.

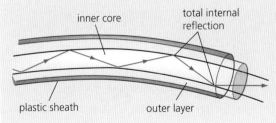

Endoscopes

Endoscopes are used by surgeons to look inside a patient's body without needing to cut a large hole.

- They consist of one bundle of optical fibres that allows light to travel into the body and then another bundle of optical fibres to allow image information to pass out of the body.
- The surgeon can therefore see on a monitor what is happening inside the body as it happens.
- The endoscope kit also carries tools for cutting, snaring, water irrigation and retrieval of tissue.
- It is the use of optical fibres that makes keyhole surgery possible.

Analogy between the behaviour of water waves and the behaviour of light

Revised

There are many similarities between the behaviour of water waves in a ripple tank and the behaviour of light. These similarities mean that we can say there is an analogy between light waves and water waves.

We can see much more happening when we look at the reflection and refraction of water waves than we can with light. For one thing, we can see that the wavelengths, frequencies and speed of the incident water waves are equal to the wavelengths, frequencies and speed of the reflected water waves. This led physicists to suspect that the wavelength, frequency and speed of light waves do not change when they reflect – and in fact this turns out to be the case.

By looking at the movement of floating chalk dust on the surface of water, we can say with confidence that water waves are transverse. This led physicists to think that light waves are transverse too – and, as we know, this is the case.

Water waves refract as they pass from deep water to shallow water – they bend towards the normal. This is also what happens when light passes from air into glass. When we measure the speed of water waves, we find that deep water waves move faster than shallow water waves. If we apply the analogy again, we would suspect that light travelling in air is moving faster than light travelling in glass. This also turns out to be the case.

The analogy is summarised in the table below.

Water waves	Light
When they reflect:	**When it reflects:**
• angle of incidence = angle of reflection	• angle of incidence = angle of reflection
• reflected wavelength = incident wavelength	• reflected wavelength = incident wavelength
• reflected frequency = incident frequency	• reflected frequency = incident frequency
• reflected speed = incident speed	• reflected speed = incident speed
When they pass from deep into shallow water:	**When it passes from air into glass and refracts:**
• they bend towards the normal	• it bends towards the normal
• refracted wavelength is less than incident wavelength	• refracted wavelength is less than incident wavelength
• refracted frequency = incident frequency	• refracted frequency = incident frequency
• refracted speed is less than incident speed	• refracted speed is less than incident speed

There are two types of lens:

1 converging (or **convex**) lenses   **2 diverging** (or **concave**) lenses

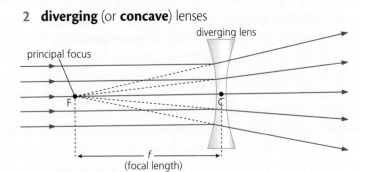

You must be able to define the **principal focus** and the **focal length** of a convex lens:

● Rays of light parallel to the principal axis of a convex (converging) lens all converge at the same point on the opposite side of the lens. This point lies on the principal axis and is called the **principal focus** (or focal point).

● The distance between the principal focus and the optical centre of a lens is called the **focal length**.

Measuring the focal length of a convex lens experimentally

To carry out this experiment you need a metre ruler, a white screen and a convex lens in a suitable holder.

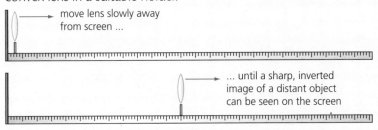

● Tape the ruler to the bench and place the white screen at the zero mark.

● Place the lens in its holder as close as possible to the screen.

● Slowly move the lens away from the screen until the image of some distant object is as sharp as possible.

● Using the metre ruler, measure the distance from the centre of the lens to the screen – this distance is the **focal length** of the lens.

Rays of light from any point on a distant object arrive at the lens as a parallel beam. Such rays will be brought to a focus in the focal plane, as shown in the figure below. This is the plane at right angles to the principal axis and containing the principal focus.

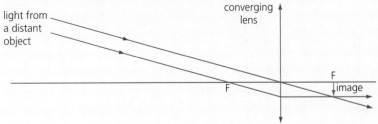

Constructing ray diagrams

You need to remember that:

● Rays of light parallel to the **principal axis** of a convex lens all converge at the same point on the principal axis (PA) on the opposite side of the lens. This point is called the **principal focus** (F).

● The distance between the principal focus and the optical centre of the lens is called the **focal length**.

● In general, the thicker the lens, the smaller the focal length.

● At GCSE the principal foci on each side of the lens are the same distance from the optical centre.

When constructing ray diagrams you should remember:

● A ray parallel to the PA is refracted through the principal focus.

● A ray through the optical centre of the lens does not refract (change its direction).

● A ray through the principal focus on one side of the lens emerges parallel to the PA on the other side of the lens.

The table below illustrates the kind of image that can be obtained with a convex lens.

Location of object	Location of image	Nature (real or virtual)	Erect or inverted?	Larger or smaller than object?	Application
Between lens and F	On same side of lens as object, but further from lens	Virtual	Erect	Larger	Magnifying glass
At F	At infinity	Real	Inverted	Larger	Searchlight
Between F and 2F	Beyond 2F	Real	Inverted	Larger	Cinema projector
At 2F	At 2F	Real	Inverted	Same size	Telescope
Just beyond 2F	Between F and 2F	Real	Inverted	Smaller	Camera
Far beyond 2F	At F	Real	Inverted	Smaller	Astronomical telescope

What are the steps in constructing a ray diagram?

Suppose an object of height 5 cm is placed 6 cm from a convex (converging) lens of focal length 4 cm and we want to find the position and height of the image. The circled numbers show the order in which the lines and rays are drawn.

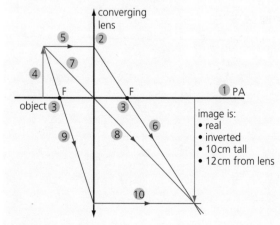

- Draw a horizontal line to represent the PA and a vertical line to represent the lens – steps 1 and 2.
- Mark the position of the principal focus with a letter F the same distance (4 cm) from the optical centre on each side of the lens – step 3.
- Draw a vertical line of height 5 cm touching the PA at the correct distance (6 cm) from the lens to represent the object – step 4.
- Draw at least two of the three possible construction rays, beginning each at the top of the object – steps 5 to 10.
- The point where the construction rays converge (or appear to converge) represents the top of the image. Draw a vertical line from this point to the PA to locate the image.

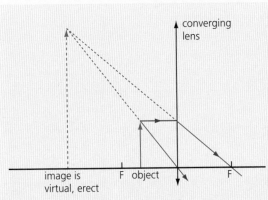

- If the object is between the principal focus and the lens then the refracted rays diverge and a virtual image is obtained.
- It is then a matter of tracing the rays backwards to locate the image.

Revision Questions

Tested

1   A stamp collector is using a magnifying glass to examine a stamp for misprints.

   a) The focal length of the lens used is 4 cm. What does this mean?   [1 mark]

   b) An object is 2 cm high and placed 2 cm from the lens. The focal length of the lens is 4 cm. On a sheet of graph paper draw a full-scale ray diagram to show how this magnifying glass forms an image of the object.   [5 marks]

   c) What is the height of the image formed?   [1 mark]

   d) How far is the image from the lens?   [1 mark]

   e) Using the same lens, how could the size of the image of this object be increased?   [1 mark]

   f) Place a tick next to any of the descriptions below that apply to the image the magnifying glass produces of this object.   [3 marks]

   Real ☐   Virtual ☐   Erect ☐

   Inverted ☐   Magnified ☐   Diminished ☐

Exam tip
When drawing ray diagrams use a sharp pencil and a ruler. And it's a good idea to have a soft pencil rubber too! Never, ever draw ray diagrams in ink!

2 Glass bricks are used to direct the natural light in some buildings. The shape of one such brick is shown below and a ray of light is incident upon it.

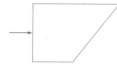

a) Continue the path of the incident ray to show how it travels through the glass brick and into the air.   [3 marks]

b) Copy and complete the table below by ticking (✔) one box in each column to show how the speed and wavelength change when the light enters the glass brick.   [2 marks]

	Speed	Wavelength
Increases		
Stays the same		
Decreases		

[2 marks]

3 A ray of light strikes mirror A as shown below.

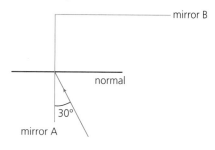

a) What is the angle of incidence at mirror A?   [1 mark]

b) What is the angle of reflection at mirror A?   [1 mark]

c) Continue the ray to show how it is reflected off both mirrors.   [2 marks]

4 Two rays of light leave a pool of water.

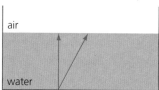

a) Continue both rays of light into the air.   [3 marks]

b) How does the speed of light change when it leaves the water?   [1 mark]

5 There are seven regions of the electromagnetic spectrum. Below are three of them.

gamma   infrared   radio

a) Write down the names of the four missing regions.   [4 marks]

b) Typical wavelengths for the three regions in the box are shown in the table. Copy and complete the table for these regions.

Region	Typical wavelength
	3 m
	1×10^{-12} m
	1×10^{-4} m

[2 marks]

6 A spherical drop of water is in the path of two rays of light. Ray B is directed at the centre C of the water drop.

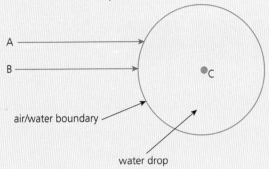

Complete the path of both rays **into** the water drop (do **not** continue out into the air again). [3 marks]

7 An object O is placed in front of a convex lens as shown below.

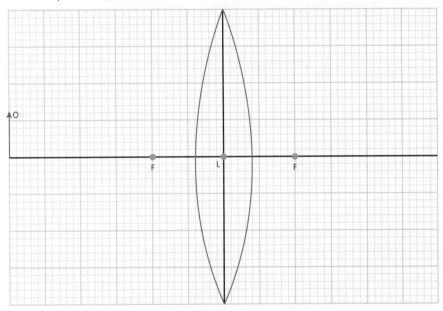

a) Copy the diagram and **using a ruler** draw rays that can be used to locate the position of the image. The image should be clearly marked. [3 marks]

b) The diagram is **full scale**. How far from the centre of the lens L is the image formed? [2 marks]

c) Which of the properties listed below describe the image formed? Ring the **three** that are correct.

Real   Virtual   Magnified   Diminished   Upright   Inverted [3 marks]

d) Describe and explain how you would measure the focal length of a convex lens. State the measurements you would take and how you would improve the accuracy of your measurements. [6 marks]

8 a) i) Draw a series of boxes like those below and write the names of the various groups of electromagnetic waves in order of increasing wavelength (as shown by the arrow). Some have been done for you.

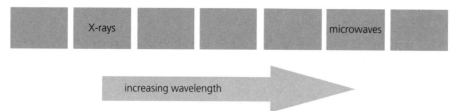

increasing wavelength

[3 marks]

ii) The microwaves used in a microwave oven have a frequency of 2.45×10^9 Hz. The speed of light is 3×10^8 m/s. Calculate the wavelength of these microwaves. **[3 marks]**

b) When an earthquake happens waves are sent out from the site of the quake. These are known as P waves and S waves. The P waves are longitudinal waves and the S waves are transverse waves.
Describe how the particles that make up the rocks of the Earth move when each type of wave passes. **[2 marks]**

9 A ray of light is shone into a rectangular glass block as shown below.

a) The critical angle for the glass is 41°. Explain what this means. **[2 marks]**

b) The path of the ray through the glass allows it to strike the shorter side. The ray meets the shorter side at an angle to the normal of 50°. Complete the diagram to show the path of the ray through and out of the glass block. **[3 marks]**

c) Explain why the light follows the path you have drawn at the side BC. **[2 marks]**

Go online for the answers Online

8 Radioactivity

Atomic structure

Revised

Atoms consist of a tiny, central nucleus around which electrons orbit in circular paths or shells. The electrons are exceedingly small in mass, with almost all of the mass of an atom being contained within the nucleus. The nucleus itself contains two different types of particle – protons and neutrons. The relative masses and charges of these three particles are shown in the table.

	Proton	Neutron	Electron
Mass (compared to proton)	1	1	negligible
Charge (compared to proton)	+1	0	−1
Location	inside nucleus	inside nucleus	orbiting nucleus

All nuclei, except the hydrogen nucleus, contain both protons and neutrons. The simplest form of atomic hydrogen has a single proton and no neutrons.

Since the only charged particles within an atom are protons and electrons, there must be **equal numbers of protons and electrons** if the atom is to be **electrically neutral**.

Nuclear radiation

Revised

In the late 19th century, Henri Becquerel discovered that uranium and many other materials with heavy atoms spontaneously and randomly emit radiations. Three different types of radiation called **alpha** (α), **beta** (β) and **gamma** (γ) **radiation** were identified. It is now known that these radiations come from the nuclei of these heavy atoms – those with a large number of protons and neutrons, whose structure is unstable. The unstable nucleus disintegrates, or **decays**, and emits radiation. The atoms that emit these radiations are said to be **radioactive**. The properties of the three types of radiation are shown in the table.

	Alpha radiation	Beta radiation	Gamma radiation
Origin	unstable nucleus	unstable nucleus	unstable nucleus
Nature	particle	particle	wave
Relative charge*	+2	−1	uncharged
Relative mass*	4	negligible	zero
Identity	helium nucleus, consisting of two protons and two neutrons	fast electron	electromagnetic wave of high energy
Ionising power	enormous	moderate	poor
Penetrating ability	stopped by 2–4 cm of air or thin tissue paper	stopped by several metres of air or about 5 mm aluminium	thick lead is an effective shield but cannot stop the radiation completely

*Relative to that of the proton

One of the early theories was the 'plum pudding' model. This saw the atom as a positively charged sphere in which the negatively charged electrons were distributed like currants in a bun, in sufficient numbers to make the atom as a whole electrically neutral.

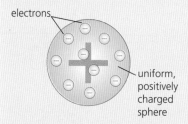

electrons

uniform, positively charged sphere

Rutherford alpha particle scattering experiment

Lord Rutherford noticed that alpha particles could be passed straight through very, very thin metal foil. He investigated this effect in detail using the apparatus below.

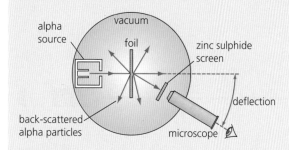

alpha source

vacuum

foil

zinc sulphide screen

deflection

back-scattered alpha particles

microscope

The alpha particles were detected by the flashes of light they produced when they hit a glass screen coated with zinc sulphide.

● The experiment had to be carried out in a vacuum to prevent collisions between alpha particles and air atoms.

● Most of the alpha particles were undeflected.

● Some alpha particles were scattered through large angles.

● A few alpha particles (about 1 in 8000) were 'back-scattered' through very large angles.

Rutherford deduced that:

● The majority of the alpha particles passed straight through the metal foil because they did not come close enough to any repulsive positive charge at all.

● All the positive charge and most of the mass of an atom formed a dense core or nucleus.

● The negative charge consisted of a 'cloud of electrons' surrounding the positive nucleus.

● Only when a positive alpha particle approached sufficiently close to a nucleus was it repelled strongly enough to rebound at large angles.

● The small size of the nucleus explained the small number of alpha particles that were repelled in this way.

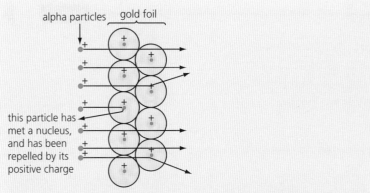

alpha particles   gold foil

this particle has met a nucleus, and has been repelled by its positive charge

↑ **Most of the alpha particles pass straight through the foil or are slightly deflected – very few make a direct hit on the nucleus because it is so small.**

Rutherford's experiment led to the abandonment of the 'plum pudding' model.

The model accepted by physicists today is called the **Rutherford–Bohr model** in honour of Rutherford and a Danish physicist called Niels Bohr who had similar ideas.

Atomic number Z and mass number A

The **atomic number, Z,** is the **number of protons** found within a nucleus. Since only protons within the nucleus are positively charged, the atomic number gives the positive charge of a nucleus. Some charged particles, such as the electron, have an 'atomic number' even though they are not found inside the nucleus – their 'atomic number' is simply their charge of –1.

The **mass number, A,** is the **total number of nucleons** to be found within a nucleus. A nucleon is a proton or a neutron. Since protons and neutrons each have a relative mass of 1, the value of A is the relative mass of the nucleus compared to the proton. Particles that are not themselves nuclei have a mass number equal to their relative mass compared to the proton. So the mass number of a proton is 1, while the mass number of an electron is 0.

All **nuclei** can be represented by a symbol of the form:

$$^A_Z X$$

where:

X is the chemical symbol for the element

A is the mass number

Z is the atomic number

Particles that are not nuclei can be represented similarly. Thus a beta particle has the symbol $^0_{-1}e$, a proton has the symbol ^1_1p, and a neutron has the symbol ^1_0n. Look back at the table on page 65 and explain why an alpha particle has the symbol $^4_2\alpha$ or ^4_2He.

Isotopes

Isotopes are **different forms** of the **same element** that have the same atomic number but **different mass number**. Isotopes come about because different forms of the same element with the same number of protons can have a different number of neutrons inside the nucleus.

Consider hydrogen as an example:

● One form of hydrogen, protium, has a single proton and no neutrons in its nucleus. It has the symbol $_1^1H$.

● Another form of hydrogen, deuterium, has one proton and one neutron in its nucleus. It has the symbol $_1^2H$.

● The third form of hydrogen, tritium, has one proton and two neutrons in its nucleus. It has the symbol $_1^3H$.

So, isotopes have the same bottom number (the atomic number) but a different top number (the mass number).

Since nuclear isotopes always refer to the same element, they are sometimes written with the **mass number** only – so you may see references to 'uranium-235' or 'iodine-131'. In such cases the number quoted is always the mass number.

> **Exam tip**
>
> Be careful with A and Z. **A** is the mass number and **Z** is the atomic number! At GCSE the number on top is never less than the number at the bottom.

Nuclear disintegration equations

The disintegration of a nucleus by radioactive decay can be represented by an equation. The uranium isotope $_{92}^{238}U$ emits an a particle, leaving behind a daughter nucleus of thorium (Th). The equation for this process is therefore:

$$_{92}^{238}U \rightarrow {}_{90}^{234}Th + {}_2^4\alpha$$

Observe that the mass numbers balance: $238 = 234 + 4$

as do the atomic numbers: $92 = 90 + 2$

Similarly, $_{92}^{234}Th$ decays by β decay, leaving behind a protactinium nucleus (Pa). The equation for this process is therefore:

$$_{90}^{234}Th \rightarrow {}_{91}^{234}Pa^* + {}_{-1}^0\beta$$

Again the mass numbers balance: $234 = 234 + 0$

As do the atomic numbers: $90 = 91 + (-1)$

Usually the daughter nucleus following α or β decay is in a highly excited state and emits a gamma (γ) ray at the same time as the α or β particle. The * in the decay equation above indicates that the protactinium is in an excited state. Since γ rays have neither mass nor charge they are, by convention, written without numbers. The emission of the γ ray is shown by the equation:

$$_{91}^{234}Pa^* \rightarrow {}_{91}^{234}Pa + \gamma$$

Background activity

Revised

One type of nuclear radiation detector is the **Geiger-Müller (GM) tube** connected to a counter. This detects and measures radiation in counts per minute. However, even when all known sources of radioactivity are removed from the laboratory, a GM counter continues to show the presence of radiation. This radiation is known as the background activity and it is always measured before any work is carried out with laboratory sources of radiation. The background activity is then subtracted from the measured count rate using the source to find the count rate from the source alone.

Background radiation comes from many sources, of which the most important are:

- radiation from the Sun
- leaks from nuclear power stations and nuclear weapons
- radiation from hospital X-ray and nuclear medicine departments
- radiation from granite rocks.

Ionisation

Revised

In a neutral atom the number of protons inside the nucleus is the same as the number of electrons orbiting the nucleus. **Ions** are electrically charged particles obtained from an atom by adding or removing electrons. The process of changing a neutral atom into an ion is called **ionisation**.

When an alpha particle, beta particle or gamma ray collides with an atom, it can remove an orbiting electron and leave behind a positive ion. Thus alpha particles, beta particles and gamma rays are called **ionising radiations**.

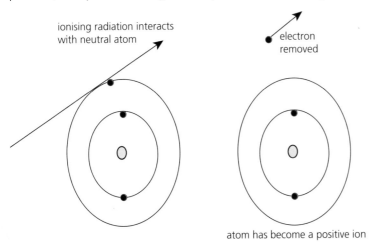

ionising radiation interacts with neutral atom

electron removed

atom has become a positive ion

↑ **Ionisation caused when an electron is removed from an atom by radiation.**

Ionising ability is related to penetrating ability. Ionisation requires energy. Highly ionising radiation loses its energy rapidly and will therefore have less penetrating ability. Weakly ionising radiation will interact little with matter and will therefore be very penetrating.

Alpha particles are the most ionising, producing about 100 000 ion-electron pairs in each centimetre of their path in air. This explains why alpha particles have such a short range (2–4 cm) in air. Gamma rays are the least ionising. Hence, they also have the greatest penetrating ability. Beta particles have moderate ionisation ability and a range between those of alpha particles and gamma rays.

The dangers of radioactivity

Alpha, beta and gamma radiation are dangerous ionising radiations. They can disrupt the DNA contained within cells and cause cancer. There are many safety regulations that must be followed concerning their use. Among the most important are:

● Except when actually being used, radioactive sources should be stored in a lead-lined box in a locked cabinet.
● Experiments should be done as quickly as possible to minimise exposure to radiation.
● Individual sources should be handled with forceps at arm's length.
● Students under 16 years old must never handle radioactive sources at all.

Hospital workers and those working in the nuclear industry also measure their exposure to radiation regularly using film badges. There is a legal limit on the amount of radiation to which people may be exposed and employers are required to ensure that their employees are suitably protected by, for example, placing sources behind thick lead shields.

Half-life

The **half-life** of a radioactive material is the **time taken for its activity to fall to half of its original value**.

> **Exam tip**
> Learn this definition so that you can quote it accurately in an exam.

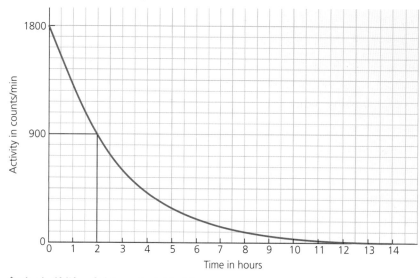

↑ The half-life of this material is 2 hours.

The **activity** of a radioactive material is measured in units called becquerels (Bq). One disintegration per second is 1 becquerel. So if a radioactive material emits 1200 α particles every minute, then 20 nuclei decay every second and its activity is 20 Bq. Calculations at GCSE are generally best solved using a table as in the example below.

Worked example 1

A certain radioisotope has a half-life of 5 days. When delivered to a hospital its activity is 5120 Bq. Find:

a) its activity 15 days after it arrives at the hospital　　[3]

b) the time taken for its activity to fall to 80 Bq　　[3]

c) its activity 10 days before it arrived at the hospital.　　[2]

Answers

a)

Activity in Bq	Number of half-lives elapsed	Time in days	Comment
5120	0	0	Arrival
2560	1	5	Every half-life causes the activity to fall to half of its previous value.
1280	2	10	
640	3	15	

So after 15 days the activity is 640 Bq.

b) We continue with the table to find the time taken to reach 80 Bq.

Activity in Bq	Number of half-lives elapsed	Time in days
640	3	15
320	4	20
160	5	25
80	6	**30**

So it takes 30 days for the activity to reach 80 Bq.

c) To find the activity 10 days before arrival, we work backwards in time.

Activity in Bq	Number of half-lives before arrival	Time in days
5 120	0	0
10 240	−1	−5
20 480	−2	−10

So, 10 days before arrival the activity was 20 480 Bq.

Uses of radioactivity in industry, medicine and agriculture

Revised

Note: Questions on radioactivity are nearly always set in the context of an application in industry, medicine or agriculture. Some of the most common applications are described below.

In industry

Radiation is used in rolling mills to control the thickness of steel, aluminium or paper. If the detector reading is too high then the product is too thin and the pressure exerted by the rollers must be reduced, and vice versa. For thick steel or aluminium a gamma source is used – these materials would absorb alpha and beta particles. Paper mills generally use beta sources – alpha particles would be absorbed while gamma radiation would pass straight through with almost no absorption. In all cases a source with a long half-life is required so that frequent source replacements are unnecessary.

Radioactive tracers are also used to **detect leaks** in underground pipes. The radioactive source is introduced upstream of the suspected leak. Detectors on the surface give a bigger reading in the vicinity of the leak. In this case the source must be a **γ-emitter** so the radiation penetrates the soil and reaches the surface. To ensure that the source quickly disappears from the soil it must have a short half-life.

Ionisation-type smoke detector

In an ionisation-type smoke detector a source of alpha radiation (often americium-241) is placed in the detector close to two electrodes. Ions are formed in the air around the radioactive source and these allow a tiny current to flow.

If there is a fire then smoke will block the path of the ions and the current falls. The fall in current is detected electronically and a siren is sounded.

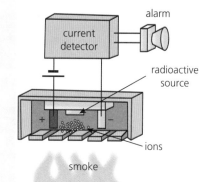

In medicine

Gamma radiation is used to **detect** and **treat** cancerous tumours, and to **sterilise surgical instruments** and **hospital dressings.**

A **diagnostic scan** may begin with an intravenous injection of a γ-emitting isotope. This accumulates in tissue and makes the tumour visible to a γ-ray camera. A computer collects and processes the image data.

A **therapeutic** (treatment) example is the destruction of cancerous tissue in the thyroid gland. A measured dose of radioactive iodine-131 is taken orally by the patient. Iodine is absorbed by the thyroid gland, and iodine-131, being a β-emitter, destroys the cancer cells there.

In agriculture

Radiation is used to study the uptake of chemicals such as phosphorus in plants, and in the destruction of bacteria and fungi on foods in order to prolong their shelf-life.

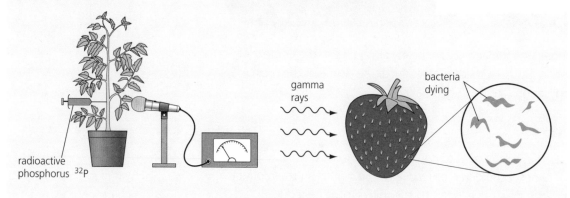

1 a) Radioactive substances emit alpha, beta and gamma radiations. Use a table like the one below to describe the nature of each of these radiations.

Radiation	Nature
Alpha (α)	
Beta (β)	
Gamma (γ)	

[3 marks]

b) A radioactive atom of uranium decays by emitting a beta (β) particle.

i) Complete the decay equation for this process by writing the appropriate numbers in the boxes.

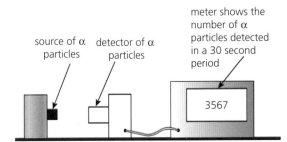

$$^{238}_{92}U \longrightarrow \boxed{}\,Np + \boxed{}\,\beta$$

[4 marks]

ii) The beta (β) decay process for this radioactive material has a half-life of 46 days. How many days pass before the activity falls by 75% of its initial value? [1 mark]

c) To measure the range of alpha (α) particles in air, the apparatus shown below was set up. The number of alpha particles reaching the detector in a 30 second period was measured at increasing distances from the source of alpha particles.

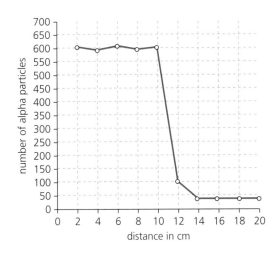

The graph below shows the results of this investigation.

The graph: number of alpha particles (y-axis, 0 to 700) vs distance in cm (x-axis, 0 to 20).

State the approximate range of α particles indicated by the graph. [1 mark]

d) In the oil industry several companies may share the same oil pipeline to transport their oil. They need to know when one company's oil stops and another company's begins. Each company adds a radioactive substance (radioisotope) to the first part of the batch of oil. A detector (Geiger counter) and counter will then show when the oil containing this radioisotope passes.

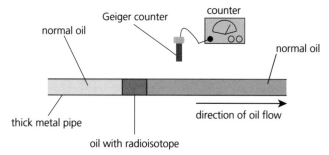

What type of radiation must be emitted by the radioisotope in the oil for this method to work? Give a reason for your answer. **[2 marks]**

e) In 1910 a historic experiment was carried out. The experiment was designed to find out more about the structure of the atom. In the experiment alpha (α) particles were directed at a very thin metal foil.

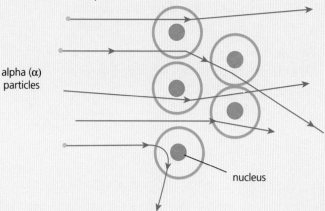

Describe and explain the observations that were made and how each one provides information on the charge, the size and the mass of the nucleus of the atom. In this question you will be assessed on your written communication skills, including the use of specialist science terms. **[6 marks]**

2 The diagram below shows a beta (β) source set up facing a detector that is connected to a counting device.

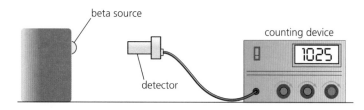

Exam tip

Usually examiners have more marking points than marks in this type of question, so the more **accurate detail** you can give, the more marks you are likely to achieve.

Describe how this apparatus could be used to measure the range of beta (β) particles in aluminium. **[5 marks]**

3 a) i) Copy and complete the diagram below, which represents a helium atom.

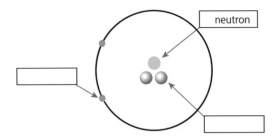

[2 marks]

ii) Helium has the chemical symbol He. Complete the symbol for the nucleus of the helium atom above by writing the appropriate numbers in the boxes.

[2 marks]

 He

b) i) A radioactive atom of uranium decays by emitting a beta (β) particle. From what part of the atom does a beta (β) particle come? [1 mark]

ii) Alpha radiation (α), beta radiation (β) and gamma radiation (γ) are all emitted by radioactive substances. Copy and complete the table below by writing a description of each type of radiation in the spaces that are blank.

Radiation	Description
Alpha (α)	
Beta (β)	
Gamma (γ)	

[3 marks]

4 a) Radioactivity consists of alpha (α) or beta (β) or gamma (γ) radiation.

   i) Which part of the atom emits these radiations? [1 mark]

   ii) Name the particles usually found in this part of the atom. [2 marks]

   iii) What is alpha (α) radiation? [1 mark]

   iv) What is beta (β) radiation? [1 mark]

   v) Which of the three radiations is the least penetrating? [1 mark]

b) Give one use of radioactivity in each of industry, medicine and agriculture. [3 marks]

c) ^1_1X is the symbol for the nucleus of an isotope of an element.
Which of the following are also isotopes of the same element?

$$^3_1X \qquad ^2_1X \qquad ^1_2X \qquad ^1_3X$$

Explain your answer. [2 marks]

5 a) Define the half-life of a radioactive substance in terms of its activity.   [1 mark]

A radioactive gas has a half-life of 52 seconds. A sample of this gas contains 2000 radioactive atoms.

   b) How many atoms of this radioactive gas will be left after 52 seconds?   [1 mark]

   c) How many atoms of this radioactive gas will be left after 104 seconds?   [1 mark]

Exam tip

The previous DAS specification had no radioactivity questions in the physics section; they were in the chemistry paper. Your exam will have radioactivity questions in P1 (Physics Paper 1).

Go online for the answers   Online

9 Fission and Fusion

Nuclear fission

Revised

Nuclear fission is the splitting up of a heavy nucleus into two or more fragments with the release of large quantities of energy. In nuclear power stations (see the photo) the nuclear fuel used for fission is usually uranium-235 or plutonium-239. The energy released is controlled and used to produce steam to drive a turbo-generator to produce electricity. The military application is to release the energy rapidly in the form of a bomb.

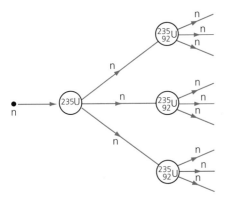

↑ **Nuclear power plant**

Nuclear fission always results in the production of very dangerous radioactive materials with long half-lives. This presents huge problems for planners and scientists. As yet we know of no safe way to store these waste products for the tens of thousands of years needed before their radioactivity decreases to an acceptably safe level. However, fission does not contribute to global warming by emitting CO_2 and this fact has increased the interest of governments in nuclear power in recent years.

For fission to occur, the uranium-235 or plutonium-239 nucleus must first absorb a neutron and then split into two lighter nuclei and release two or three fission neutrons.

Fission comes about as a result of the heavy nucleus being struck by a slow neutron. The heavy nucleus splits and the fragments move apart at very high speed, carrying with them vast amounts of energy. At the same time, two or three fast neutrons are also emitted – these are the **fission neutrons**. The fission neutrons go on to produce further fission and so create a chain reaction.

> ### Exam tip
> Make sure you spell the words correctly. Fission is the splitting of a heavy nucleus, while fusion is the combining of two or more light nuclei to make a heavy nucleus.

↑ **A chain reaction in uranium-235**

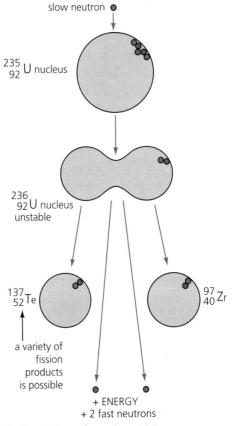

↑ **The fission of uranium-235**

Nuclear energy is a controversial topic. Those in favour of it point to the fact that it can produce vast amounts of electricity without producing carbon dioxide and contributing to **global warming**. Those against it say that the by-product of nuclear energy – nuclear waste – has created one of the greatest problems of the 20th century.

Germany decided in 2011 to **phase out** all of its **nuclear reactors** by 2022. In the period up to 2022, it will invest heavily in **renewable energy**.

The decision was prompted by a nuclear accident in Japan. This started in March 2011, when an earthquake and tsunami damaged several reactors in Fukushima, Japan, leading to a nuclear meltdown and a serious release of radiation. Following that accident, Angela Merkel, the German Prime Minister (Chancellor), who has a PhD in physics, said: 'We have to follow a new path'.

Germany's decision to abandon nuclear power comes at a time when many nations are planning to build more nuclear reactors. Before the Japanese nuclear accident, the USA was planning to build 100 new nuclear power stations. Meanwhile, France has 56 working nuclear power stations, generating 76% of its electricity. Its decision to have so many nuclear power stations dates back to 1973 and the quadrupling of the price of oil by some Arab nations. At that time most of France's electricity came from oil-burning power stations. France had no oil, no gas and almost no coal resources. Over the following 35 years, France installed 56 nuclear reactors, satisfying its power needs and even **exporting electricity** to other European countries. A popular French answer to the question of why they have so much nuclear energy is: 'No oil, no gas, no coal, no choice.'

Nuclear waste is an enormously difficult political problem, which to date no country has solved. Radioactive waste is extremely dangerous, and expensive measures must be taken to store it until the level of activity is sufficiently small. In some cases, this means that the waste must be stored deep underground in a **vitrified** (glass-like) state for tens of thousands of years. The danger is that over time the containers may leak and cause underground water pollution. A further danger comes from earthquakes – these can rupture containers of radioactive waste buried underground, causing the radioactive material to leak into the soil and contaminate water sources.

Nuclear fusion

Nuclear fusion is the combination of light nuclei (such as hydrogen) to form a heavier nucleus (such as helium) with the release of vast quantities of energy. It is the process that takes place in most stars, including our Sun.

Nuclei tend to repel each other, as they are positively charged. Joining nuclei together requires them to collide at enormously high speeds to overcome this **electrical repulsion force**. To get the nuclei to move fast enough requires temperatures of many millions of degrees. This presents problems that physicists have so far been unable to solve.

One problem is **containment** – no reaction vessel can survive these enormously high temperatures.

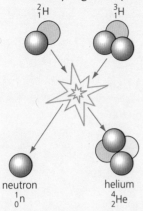

^2_1H ^3_1H

neutron
^1_0n

helium
^4_2He

$$^2_1H + {}^3_1H \rightarrow {}^4_2He + {}^1_0n + energy$$

Fusion of hydrogen nuclei looks very attractive in the longer term. It produces no serious radiation hazard (unlike fission) and the raw material (hydrogen) can easily be extracted from seawater, which is in abundant supply on Earth. In addition, it produces no harmful greenhouse gases. One of the most promising research projects is the fusion of deuterium and tritium to produce helium. A neutron is also produced as a waste product.

The really exciting idea is this: nuclear fusion has the potential to solve the energy needs of the whole world, provided the technological difficulties of fusion reactors (high temperature and containment) can be overcome.

Worked example 1

Discuss briefly the political issues relating to nuclear fission. Make three major points. [6]

Answer

Nuclear power stations provide employment for many thousands of people worldwide, not only directly in the power stations themselves, but also in support functions such as transport and **reprocessing of nuclear material**.

However, nuclear fission reactors produce large amounts of dangerously **radioactive waste products** with **very long half-lives**. These have to be stored for tens of thousands of years, deep underground in secure locations. Most people do not want these materials to be stored near them. This is the NIMBY (NOT IN MY BACK YARD) principle.

In addition, the equipment needed to produce the **uranium isotopes** for a nuclear power station can readily be modified to make the fuel required for a nuclear bomb, thus increasing the spread of nuclear weapons. This is a politically sensitive issue at the moment in respect of Iran's desire to build and run its own nuclear power plant.

1   Some scientists believe that we should make greater use of nuclear fission. Describe what happens in the fission of $^{235}_{92}$U in a nuclear reactor.   **[6 marks]**

2   Describe the nuclear process that happens in the interior of our Sun.   **[6 marks]**

3   In some electricity power stations, energy is released during a process that uses uranium.
   a) i)   What is the name of this process?   **[1 mark]**

   ii)   Which part of the uranium atom is involved in the release of energy?   **[1 mark]**

   iii) What happens to this part of the uranium atom during the process?   **[1 mark]**

   One of the substances resulting from this process is strontium (symbol Sr). This is an unstable element and it decays by beta (β) emission to the element yttrium (symbol Y).

   iv)   Complete the equation below for this decay. Write the appropriate numbers in the boxes provided.

   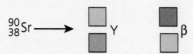

   $^{90}_{38}$Sr $\longrightarrow$ $\square \atop \square$ Y $\square \atop \square$ β

   [4 marks]

   b) i)   Name the process that is the source of the Sun's energy.   **[1 mark]**

   ii)   Describe this process, briefly, stating the type of atom and the part of the atom involved.   **[2 marks]**

4   **a)**   The apparatus shown below is used to investigate the radiation emitted from a radioactive source. Different materials are placed between the radioactive source and the detector. For each material the count rate is measured and then the background count rate is taken into account.

   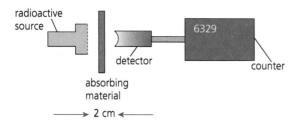

   i)   Where does this background count rate come from?   **[1 mark]**

   ii)   How is the background count rate taken into account when working out the true count rate in this experiment?   **[1 mark]**

   The count rates, after background count rate has been taken into account, are shown below.

Absorbing material	Count rate in counts per minute
Air	800
Thin sheet of paper	802
3 mm thick aluminium sheet	412
5 mm thick lead sheet	45

   It is known that this radioactive source emits two types of radiation.

   iii) Which two radiations does the source emit? Explain your answer.   **[4 marks]**

b) Gold has a radioactive isotope with the symbol $^{195}_{79}$Au.

   i) How many particles are there in the nucleus of this gold isotope? **[1 mark]**

   ii) How many of these particles are neutrons? **[2 marks]**

Doctors use this isotope as a tracer to monitor the way in which a patient's heart works. The isotope is injected into a person's bloodstream.

The half-life of this isotope is 30 seconds. The initial activity of the sample containing the isotope is 512 counts per second.

   iii) Calculate how long it takes for the activity of the sample to decrease to 32 counts per second. Give your answer in minutes. **[3 marks]**

   iv) Explain why an isotope with a half-life of 30 minutes would be unsuitable for this use. **[2 marks]**

c) Some places have a high level of radiation caused by radon gas escaping from underground rocks. The rocks contain radium (Ra), which is radioactive and decays into radon (Rn). Radon is also radioactive.

   i) Complete the decay equation below for this process by inserting the correct number or symbol in the boxes provided. **[4 marks]**

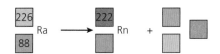

   ii) Radon has a short half-life and it emits alpha particles. Explain why the presence of radon **gas** in buildings is a health hazard. **[2 marks]**

d) i) Nuclear fusion is the joining of light atoms to produce heavier atoms and release energy. Why is this statement incorrect? **[1 mark]**

   ii) Nuclear fusion and nuclear fission are both sources of energy.

   Which source of energy is used in the generation of electricity?

   Which is the source of energy in the stars? **[2 marks]**

Go online for the answers — Online

10 Electricity

Conductors, semiconductors and insulators Revised

Experiments show that there are three types of materials with different electrical properties: **good conductors**, **semiconductors** and **poor conductors (insulators)**. Good conductors have many free electrons and insulators have almost none. Semiconductors have very few free electrons at room temperature, but considerably more at high temperatures. Examples of each type of material are given in the table.

Good conductors	Semiconductors	Insulators
Silver	Silicon	Plastic
Copper	Germanium	Rubber
Aluminium		Wood
Steel		Cork

Static electricity Revised

● When two insulators are rubbed together they **both** become electrically charged. This is because negatively charged electrons rub off one material on to the other. The material that gains electrons becomes negatively charged. The material that loses electrons becomes positively charged. Notice, however, that in every case **only electrons move**. Positive charges **do not** move.

● When a **polythene rod** is rubbed with a cloth, electrons are taken off the cloth (which now has a shortage of electrons and is therefore **positively** charged) and transferred to the polythene rod (which now has a surplus of electrons and is therefore **negatively** charged).

● When a **cellulose acetate rod** is rubbed with a cloth, electrons are taken off the rod (which now has a shortage of electrons and is therefore **positively** charged) and transferred to the cloth (which now has a surplus of electrons and is therefore **negatively** charged).

● A **charged conductor** can be discharged by connecting it to earth with a metal (conducting) wire or chain. The surplus electrons move down the chain to earth if the conductor is negatively charged. If the conductor is positively charged, electrons flow up from the earth.

● The Law of Static Electricity states that **opposite charges attract** each other, while objects with the **same charge repel** each other.

● Charged objects can attract uncharged objects – for example, the charged screen of a television attracts dust. You should be able to explain this phenomenon in terms of **polarisation**.

When a positively charged rod is brought near a tiny piece of aluminium foil, the free electrons in the foil are pulled towards the rod, creating a surplus of electrons at the top of the foil and a deficiency of electrons at the bottom of the foil. This is called **polarisation**.

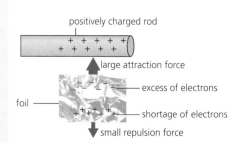

positively charged rod

large attraction force

excess of electrons

foil

shortage of electrons

small repulsion force

Consequently, the top of the foil is attracted to the rod, because unlike charges attract. But like charges repel, so the positive charge at the bottom of the foil is repelled. The attraction forces are stronger than the repulsion forces because the attracting charge is closer to the rod than the repelling charge. As a result there is a net upward attraction force between the rod and the foil.

Dangers of static electricity

Static electricity is a nuisance and can pose a hazard:

- in an electric storm (lightning)
- in grain chutes
- when refuelling aircraft and road vehicles with flammable liquids
- when loading and unloading oil tankers
- in integrated circuits inside computers

Lightning is an electrical discharge between a charged cloud and the Earth. Buildings can be protected against lightning by a **lightning conductor**. This is a long strip of copper metal with a spike at the top, running the length of the building and terminating in the ground.

In grain chutes there can be an accumulation of dust and electric charge. An electrical discharge can result in a spark, leading to a fire. There is a similar danger with flammable fuels. In both cases the solution is to **earth** all metal parts to prevent charge accumulation.

Computer engineers wear **earthed wrist straps** to reduce the possibility of destroying computer chips.

Current in a simple circuit

Revised

Inside an electrical cell, chemical reactions occur that push electrons out from the negative terminal and pull electrons in at the positive terminal. In the 19th century scientists thought that an electric current was a flow of positive charge from the positive terminal of the battery to the negative terminal. This idea was wrong, but the picture that a current is from positive to negative remained. Today we say that:

- **conventional current** flows from **positive** to **negative**
- **electrons** flow from **negative** to **positive.**

Charge and current

The quantity of charge, Q, is measured in units called coulombs, C. Electric current, I, is the rate at which charge flows in a circuit. The charge equation is therefore:

$$Q = It \qquad \text{or} \qquad I = \frac{Q}{t}$$

where:

Q = charge, in C, passing a fixed point

I = current in amperes (A)

t = time taken in seconds (s)

Worked example 1

A current of 0.5 A flows through a resistor. What charge passes through the resistor in 3 minutes? [4]

Exam tip

Remember time must be measured in seconds.

Answer

$Q = It = 0.5 \times (3 \times 60) = 0.5 \times 180 = 90\,C$

Revision Questions

Tested

1 How much current is flowing if a charge of 500 mC passes a fixed point in 25 seconds?

[3 marks]

Exam tip

$Q = It$ is an easy equation to use as long as you remember to convert from millicoulombs to coulombs and from minutes to seconds.

2 A current of 20 µA flows through a woman's body for 10 ms. Calculate the total amount of charge which has passed through her body. [3 marks]

3 A current of 32 mA flows for 1 second in an electrical circuit.
   a) Write down in coulombs the amount of charge that leaves the battery in 1 second.
   [1 mark]

   b) The charge on one electron is -1.6×10^{-19} C. Calculate the number of electrons that leave the negative terminal of the battery in 1 second. [3 marks]

Go online for the answers

Online

11 Circuit Diagrams and Symbols

An electrical circuit may be represented by a circuit diagram with symbols for the components. Circuit diagrams are easy to understand and are universally understood.

Below are the electrical symbols you must know and recognise.

Component	Symbol	Component	Symbol
cell		ammeter	(A)
battery		voltmeter	(V)
resistor		diode	
switch		variable resistor	
lamp		fuse	

Measuring current and voltage
Revised

The long, thin line in the symbol for a cell is the positive terminal. The short, fat line is the negative terminal.

Current **through** a component is measured using an **ammeter** placed **in series** with it.

Voltage is measured **across** a component using a **voltmeter in parallel** with it. The words **potential difference** or **PD** mean exactly the same as voltage.

The arrows on the diagram opposite show the direction in which conventional current flows.

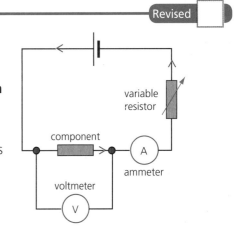

Joining cells in series
Revised

When we join cells in series, plus to minus, the cell voltages add up. For example, when two 1.5 volt cells are joined together they supply a total voltage of 3 V. If the cells are connected the wrong way round they cancel each other out and we get no voltage at all!

When joining cells in series we must pay attention to cell polarity. We always join a plus (long, thin line) to a minus (short, fat line).

If two identical lamps are connected in series across a 1.5 V cell, they are generally equally dim and much dimmer than when there is only a single lamp. Why should this be? The reason is that the voltage across each lamp is now only half of the cell's voltage. This in turn means that the current through each lamp is less than before, so it burns less brightly.

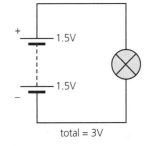

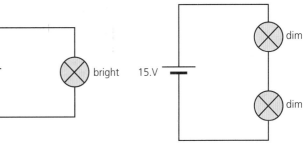

This law states that the current through many conductors is directly proportional to the voltage across it, provided the temperature remains constant. You should remember what the law states and get lots of practice at using it. As an equation, Ohm's law can be written:

$V = I \times R$

where:

V = voltage across component in volts (V)

I = current through component in amperes (A)

R = resistance of the component in ohms (Ω).

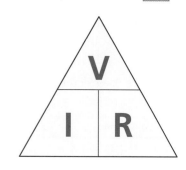

For those materials that obey Ohm's law (like metals), the graph of voltage against current is a straight line through the origin, see the example on the right.

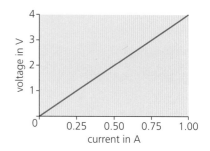

Current-voltage graphs for non-ohmic materials

Most materials do not obey Ohm's law. For such materials it is customary to show behaviour in the form of a current–voltage graph. Two devices are of particular interest.

The resistance of **filament lamps** increases as the current increases. This is because the increasing current in the lamp increases the temperature of the filament and hence increases the filament's resistance.

The graph opposite shows how the resistance of the filament rises from $5\,\Omega$ to $15\,\Omega$ when the current increases from 0.2 A to 0.4 A.

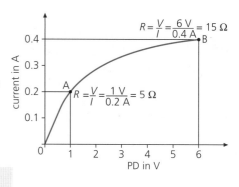

Diodes are devices made from specially treated silicon. They get their name from the words '**di**rectional **de**vices'. They allow current to flow readily (i.e. low resistance) in one direction, but let (almost) no current flow in the reverse direction (very high resistance). Current in a diode flows only in the direction of the arrow, as shown below.

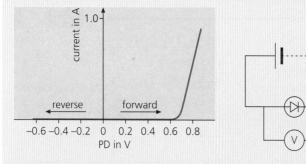

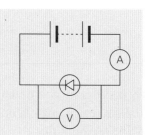

The diode above is **forward biased**. It allows current to flow readily.

The diode on the right is **reverse biased**. It does not allow current to flow readily.

Worked example 1

The current in a light bulb is 0.4 A when the voltage across it is
1.6 V. Calculate the resistance of the bulb's filament. [4]

Answer

First write down the relevant equation: $V = I \times R$

Then make the substitutions: $1.6 = 0.4 \times R$

A little arithmetic: $R = \dfrac{1.6}{0.4} = 4$

And don't forget the unit: Resistance $= 4\,\Omega$

Resistors in series

Revised

The total resistance of two or more resistors in series is the sum of the
individual resistances.

$R_{total} = R_1 + R_2 + R_3 + \ldots$

In the combination opposite, the three resistors could be replaced with a
single resistance of $4 + 8 + 6 = 18\,\Omega$.

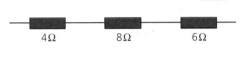

$4\Omega \qquad 8\Omega \qquad 6\Omega$

total resistance = 18 Ω

Resistors in parallel

Revised

When two **equal** resistors are placed in parallel, their combined resistance
is half the resistance of one of them. The parallel combination opposite
therefore has a resistance of $\dfrac{6}{2} = 3\,\Omega$.

Foundation students need only know how to calculate the total resistance
of two equal, parallel resistors.

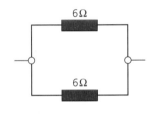

6Ω

6Ω

total resistance = 3 Ω

Higher Tier GCSE Physics and DAS students need to know what to do
if there are more than two resistors (or if the resistances are not equal).
Then you should use the equation:

$$\frac{1}{R_{total}} = \frac{1}{R_1} + \frac{1}{R_2} + \frac{1}{R_3} + \ldots$$

For the combination opposite:

$$\frac{1}{R_{total}} = \frac{1}{R_1} + \frac{1}{R_2} + \frac{1}{R_3} + \ldots = \frac{1}{6} + \frac{1}{3} = \frac{3}{6} = \frac{1}{2}$$

So, $R_{total} = \dfrac{2}{1} = 2\,\Omega$.

There are two common mistakes made by candidates. The first is
to misquote the equation as $R_{total} = \dfrac{1}{R_1} + \dfrac{1}{R_2} + \dfrac{1}{R_3} + \ldots$ (doing this
always gets zero marks). The second is forgetting to turn the final fraction
upside down (thus getting a final answer of $0.5\,\Omega$ rather than $2\,\Omega$ in the
example above).

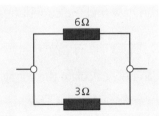

6Ω

3Ω

In a series circuit:

- all components are connected in a line, like carriages in a train
- the current in every component in series is the same
- disconnecting any component means:
    - there is no longer a complete circuit
    - all current stops flowing
- the voltages across the components add up to the battery voltage
- voltages across identical components are the same.

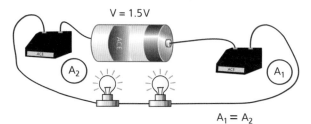

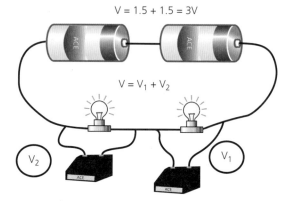

In the circuit below, the total resistance is:

$$R_{total} = R_1 + R_2 + R_3 = 3 + 4 + 5 = 12\,\Omega$$

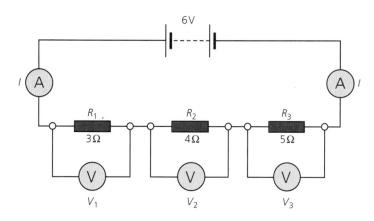

We can now find the current from the battery using Ohm's law:

$$I_{battery} = \frac{V_{battery}}{R_{circuit}} = \frac{6}{12} = 0.5\,A$$

We can now calculate the voltage across each resistor:

$3\,\Omega$: $V = IR = 0.5 \times 3 = 1.5\,V$

$4\,\Omega$: $V = IR = 0.5 \times 4 = 2\,V$

$5\,\Omega$: $V = IR = 0.5 \times 5 = 2.5\,V$

Note also how the sum of the voltages across the resistors
$(1.5\,V + 2\,V + 2.5\,V) = 6\,V$, which is the battery voltage.

In a parallel circuit:

- all components are connected across the battery independently
- the voltage across each component is equal to that of the battery
- the current in different components is different
- disconnecting any component has no effect on the current in the other components
- the sum of the currents through the components is equal to that taken from the battery.

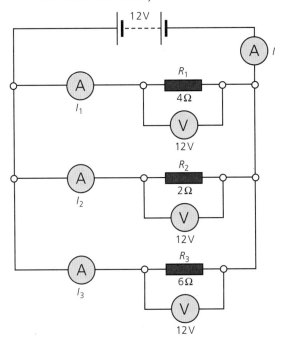

In the parallel circuit above, the voltage across each resistor is the battery voltage (12 V). Using Ohm's law we can calculate the current in each resistor:

$4\,\Omega: I = \dfrac{V}{R} = \dfrac{12}{4} = 3\,A$

$2\,\Omega: I = \dfrac{V}{R} = \dfrac{12}{2} = 6\,A$

$6\,\Omega: I = \dfrac{V}{R} = \dfrac{12}{6} = 2\,A$

Hence the current from the battery = sum of currents in parallel sections

$$= 3 + 6 + 2 = 11\,A$$

We can use this to find the resistance of the circuit from:

$R = \dfrac{V_{battery}}{I_{battery}} = \dfrac{12}{11}\,\Omega.$

(This can be confirmed from $\dfrac{1}{R_{total}} = \dfrac{1}{R_1} + \dfrac{1}{R_2} + \dfrac{1}{R_3} = \dfrac{1}{4} + \dfrac{1}{2} + \dfrac{1}{6} = \dfrac{11}{12}$

So, $R_{total} = \dfrac{12}{11}\,\Omega$.)

Exam tip

In a **S**eries circuit, the current is the **S**ame everywhere. In a **P**arallel circuit, the current s**P**lits.

Short circuits

A switch in parallel with any component can cause a short circuit. When the switch is closed, current flows through the switch and not through the component. This generally decreases the resistance of the circuit and increases the current drawn from the power supply. A short circuit may cause a fire. GCSE examiners ask questions involving the calculation of resistance in circuits involving a short circuit. A worked example is given below.

Worked example 2

a) Three 20 Ω resistors are connected between X and Y as shown.

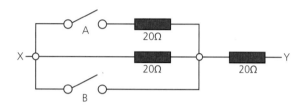

Complete the following table to show the effective resistance between X and Y for the different positions of the switches.   [4]

Switch		Resistance between X and
A	B	Y (in Ω)
Open	Open	
Closed	Open	
Open	Closed	
Closed	Closed	

b) The current flowing through the bulb in circuit A opposite is 0.3 A. A second resistor is added as shown to form circuit B.

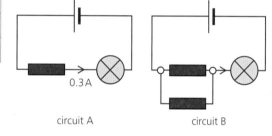

circuit A   circuit B

i)   How will the current in the bulb change when this resistor is added?   [1]

ii) How does the brightness of the bulb in circuit B compare with the brightness of the bulb in circuit A?   [1]

Answers

a)

Switch		Resistance between X	
A	B	and Y (in Ω)	Comment
Open	Open	40	Central and right 20 Ω resistors are in series.
Closed	Open	30	Two 20 Ω resistors in parallel are in series with right 20 Ω resistor.
Open	Closed	20	When B is closed, the two parallel 20 Ω resistors are **short-circuited** – only the right 20 Ω resistor is connected between X and Y.
Closed	Closed	20	

b) i)   Current increases (total circuit resistance decreases).

ii) Bulb in B is brighter.

The factors affecting resistance

The resistance of a conductor at constant temperature depends on three factors:

- **Length:** resistance is **directly proportional** to the length of the conductor. A graph of resistance against length is a straight line through the origin.

- **Cross-sectional area:** resistance is **inversely proportional** to the area of the conductor. A graph of resistance against $\frac{1}{area}$ is a straight line through the origin.

- **Material:** metals have low resistance; non-metals have high resistance.

Investigating how these factors affect resistance

The resistance of a metallic conductor at constant temperature depends on length

(Controlled: cross-sectional area and material)

- Measure and cut off 1 metre of nichrome resistance wire.

- Attach it with sticky tape to a metre ruler – make sure there are no kinks in the wire.

- Measure and record the current through and the voltage across 40 cm of the nichrome wire. Use Ohm's law to calculate its resistance.

- Repeat this process for increasing lengths of the wire up to 1.0 m.

- Be careful to switch off the current between measurements to ensure that the temperature of the wire does not increase.

- Record your results in a table as shown below.

Length in cm	Voltage in V	Current in A	Resistance in Ω

A graph of resistance against length is a straight line through the origin, showing that the resistance is directly proportional to the length.

The resistance of a metallic conductor at constant temperature depends on the cross-sectional area

(Controlled: length and material)

- Use a micrometer screw gauge to measure the diameter, D, in mm, and then calculate the cross-sectional area, using cross-sectional area $= \frac{\pi D^2}{4}$

- Repeat this process for five further thicknesses of the same length of wire and same type of material.

- For each thickness, measure and record the current through it and the voltage across it.

- Use Ohm's law to determine the resistance for that thickness.

- Record your results in a table as shown on page 92.

Area in mm²	Voltage in V	Current in A	Resistance in Ω	1/cross-sectional in mm⁻²

A graph of resistance (*y*-axis) versus the reciprocal of the cross-sectional area (*x*-axis) should give a straight line through the origin, showing that the resistance of a wire is inversely proportional to its cross-sectional area.

The resistance of a metallic conductor at constant temperature depends on the material it is made from

(Controlled: length and thickness)

● Using 1 metre of 32 SWG copper wire, measure and record the resistance as before.

● Repeat the process using the same dimensions of wires such as steel, nichrome and constantan.

Energy in electrical circuits
Revised

When an electric current flows, free electrons move through the conductor from the negative terminal of the battery to the positive terminal. As they do so they collide with vibrating atoms in the metal. In these collisions kinetic energy is passed from the electrons to the atoms, causing them to vibrate with greater amplitude. The result is that **heat energy** is generated and the temperature of the conductor increases.

Electrical charge (*Q*) only flows through a resistor when there is a voltage (*V*) across that resistor. The electrical energy (*E*) produced in the resistor is given by the equation:

$E = Q \times V$

where:

E = energy in joules

Q = charge in coulombs

and *V* = voltage in volts.

Exam tip

This equation must be memorised. It tells us that when a charge of 1 C flows through a resistor and produces 1 J of heat energy, then the voltage across that resistor is 1 volt.

Worked example 3

The potential difference between a cloud and the ground is 150 000 volts. A bolt of lightning from the cloud carries a charge of 250 C. How much electrical energy is contained in the bolt of lightning? [4]

Answer

Energy $E = Q \times V$

$= 250 \times 150\,000$

$= 37\,500\,000\,J$

$= 37.5\,MJ$

Joule's law can be obtained by combining the equation above with the equation for current ($Q = It$) and dividing by time t. It refers to the power (P) (or energy converted per second) in a resistor caused by an electrical current. Joule's law can be written in three different ways:

$$P = IV \quad \text{or} \quad P = I^2R \quad \text{or} \quad P = \frac{V^2}{R}$$

where:

P = energy converted per second in watts (or joules per second)
I = current in resistor in amperes
V = voltage across resistor in volts
R = resistance of resistor in ohms.

The second and third forms of Joule's law ($P = I^2R$ and $P = \frac{V^2}{R}$) can be obtained from the first ($P = IV$) by combining it with Ohm's law ($V = IR$).

Exam tip

All these equations should be memorised by Higher candidates.

Note that only the **first** form of Joule's law is required for Foundation candidates (GCSE Physics and DAS) and they need to be able to use it to calculate **power**, **current** and **voltage**. (But they can simply substitute the numbers; they are not required to rearrange the symbols.)

Worked example 4

1 Calculate the current flowing in a 60 W electric light bulb when connected to a 240 V supply. [3]

2 Find the voltage across an immersion heater rated 2880 W if the resistance of the element is 20 Ω. [4]

3 Find the current in an electric toaster rated 1440 W if the resistance of the element is 40 Ω. [4]

Exam tip

This example shows the usefulness of Joule's law. By remembering the third form of Joule's law the problem can be solved easily.

Answers

1 $P = IV$

$60 = I \times 240$

$I = \dfrac{60}{240} = 0.25\,\text{A}$

2 $P = \dfrac{V^2}{R}$ (Joule's law)

So, $V^2 = RP = 20 \times 2880$

$V^2 = 57\,600$

$V = \sqrt{57600}$

$V = 240\ \text{volts}$

3 $P = I^2R$ (Joule's law)

So, $I^2 = \dfrac{P}{R} = \dfrac{1440}{40}$

$I^2 = 36$

$I = \sqrt{36}$

$I = 6\,\text{A}$

1 **a)** The diagram shows a balloon becoming charged with static
electricity by being rubbed backwards and forwards across hair.

Explain fully how the balloon becomes positively
charged. **[4 marks]**

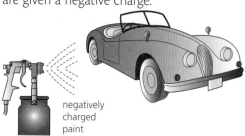

b) Electrostatic charges are used in paint spraying. The paint droplets
are given a negative charge.

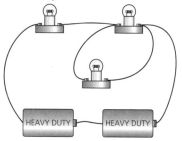

negatively
charged
paint

i) Explain why the paint droplets from the spray gun spread out. **[1 mark]**

ii) What charge should the car be given for most effective painting? **[1 mark]**

iii) Explain your answer to **ii)**. **[1 mark]**

c) Draw a circuit diagram to represent the circuit shown below. You must use the
correct symbols.

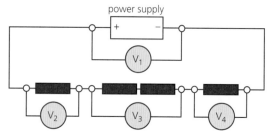

HEAVY DUTY   HEAVY DUTY

[3 marks]

2 A pupil investigates the current flowing in a circuit. The pupil uses three **identical** resistors.
When the switch S is closed, a current of 60 mA flows through the circuit at X.

power supply

> **Exam tip**
>
> Always ask yourself why the
> examiner has put some words in
> bold type. It means that these words
> are very, very important!

a) Copy and complete the following table to indicate the currents flowing through ammeters
A_1, A_2 and A_3.

Current in A_1	Current in A_2	Current in A_3
mA	mA	mA

[3 marks]

The pupil now measures voltages in a different circuit. The pupil uses four **identical** resistors.
Voltmeter V_1 reads 24 V.

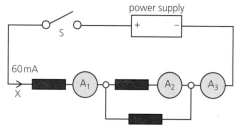

power supply

b) Complete the following table to indicate the other voltmeter readings.

Voltmeter V_1	Voltmeter V_2	Voltmeter V_3	Voltmeter V_4
24 V	V	V	V

[3 marks]

3 What are the resistances of the combinations of 6 Ω resistors shown below?

a)

b)

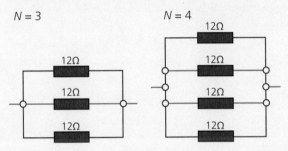

[2 marks]

4 Liam is investigating the relationship between the total resistance, R, of a number of equal resistors in parallel and the number of resistors, N. He sets up the following arrangements of resistors and then measures their total resistance.

N = 3   N = 4

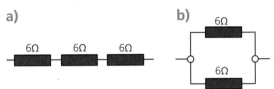

a) Calculate the resistance of each of the parallel circuits above and use your answers to complete the table.

Number of resistors, N	2	3	4	5
Total resistance, R, in Ω				2.4

[3 marks]

b) What is the mathematical relationship between R and Ṅ? [1 mark]

c) Use your answer to part **b)** to predict the total resistance of 24 resistors, each of resistance 12 Ω, connected in parallel with each other. [1 mark]

5 Ben sets up the circuit in the diagram below using two resistors and a switch. The switch S is open.

a) What current flows through the ammeter? [1 mark]

b) What is the voltage across the 6 Ω resistor? [1 mark]

The switch S is now closed.

c) What is the total resistance of the circuit? [1 mark]

d) Calculate the current flowing through the ammeter. [3 marks]

e) Calculate the voltage across the 3 Ω resistor. [1 mark]

6 a) Draw a circuit diagram in which two bulbs are in parallel and controlled by a single switch. **[2 marks]**

b) An electric switch is made up as shown in the diagram below. The terminals are made of brass, the flexible strip of plastic and the base of copper.

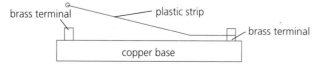

brass terminal — plastic strip

brass terminal

copper base

i) What **two** mistakes have been made by the maker of the switch? **[2 marks]**

ii) Explain how **one** of these mistakes prevents the switch from working properly. **[2 marks]**

c) Large amounts of electric charge can collect on clouds. What danger can this cause for tall buildings beneath the clouds? **[1 mark]**

d) Two balloons have been rubbed until they are electrically charged. The diagram shows the two balloons hanging side by side.

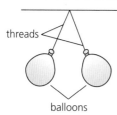

threads

balloons

i) What can you tell about the charge on the balloons? **[1 mark]**

ii) Explain your answer. **[1 mark]**

Go online for the answers ─────────────────────────── Online

12 Wiring a Plug

You need to know how to assemble, correctly wired, a three-pin plug.
A mains electricity cable contains **two** or **three** colour-coded inner wires.

blue wire	neutral
brown wire	live
green and yellow stripes wire	earth

- There is a **fuse** between the **live terminal** and the live pin.
- The fuse heats up, melts and **breaks the circuit** if too much current flows.
- The cable is secured in the plug by a cable grip.

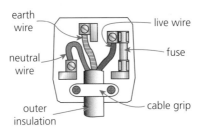

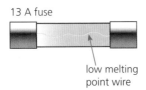

There is an easy way to remember where each wire goes:
- blue (neutral) goes **left**
- brown (live) goes **right**
- green/yellow striped (earth) goes to the **top**.

- Fuses in plugs are made in standard ratings. The most common are 1 A, 3 A, 5 A and 13 A. The fuse used should blow at a slightly higher current than the device needs.
- If the device works at less than 1 A, use a 1 A fuse.
- If the device works at between 1 A and 3 A, use a 3 A fuse.
- If the device works at between 3 A and 5 A, use a 5 A fuse.
- If the device works at 5 A or more, use a 13 A fuse.

The fuse must **always** be on the **live** side of the plug. If the fuse was on the neutral side then the appliance would still be at a dangerously **high voltage** even when the fuse blows.

Question **1a) iii)** in the Revision questions is about using Joule's law to calculate the correct fuse for an appliance.

Electrical appliances such as cookers and washing machines have metal cases. If the live wire inside an appliance such as a cooker comes loose and touches the metal casing, you could get an electric shock. However, the **earth terminal** is connected to the metal casing, so the current goes through the earth wire instead of causing an electric shock. The earth wire has a very low resistance, so the current through it is very large. This breaks the fuse and disconnects the appliance. The **earth wire** protects the user by providing a safe route for the current to flow through if the live wire touches the casing.

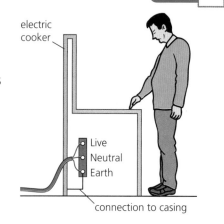

electric cooker

Live
Neutral
Earth

connection to casing

Double insulation

Appliances such as radios and computer printers have plastic casings and therefore they do not have an earth wire. The casing cannot give an electric shock, even if the wires inside touch it. These appliances have all their metal parts in a separate plastic box, so that the user can never touch a conductor at a high voltage. These appliances are **double insulated**, which is indicated by the symbol shown opposite.

Always switch and fuse on the live side

Fuses and switches are **always** wired into the **live side**. If they were in the neutral side then the appliance would be 'live' even when the fuse had blown or the appliance was switched off. It would then be possible to get an electrical shock even when the appliance was switched off!

In most two-storey houses you can turn the landing lights on or off from upstairs or downstairs. To do this we need a two-way switch, as illustrated here.

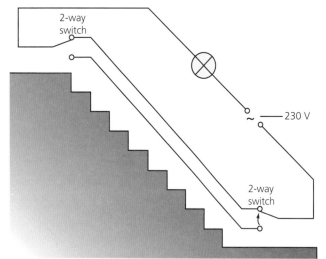

2-way switch

230 V

2-way switch

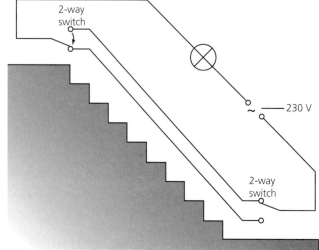

2-way switch

230 V

2-way switch

Paying for electricity

Electricity companies bill customers in units known as kilowatt-hours (kWh). 1 kWh is the amount of energy used by an electrical appliance rated 1000 W in 1 hour. We calculate the amount of energy used in kWh using the equation:

number of kWh = number of kilowatts × number of hours

> **Exam tip**
> This formula must be memorised.

Worked example 1

Calculate the cost of running a 3000 W immersion heater for 8 hours if electricity costs 11 pence per kWh.   [3]

Answer

Number of kWh = number of kilowatts × number of hours
        = 3 × 8 = 24 kWh
Cost = 24 kWh @ 11 pence each
        = 24 × 11 = 264 pence = £2.64

Alternating current and direct current

A **direct current (d.c.)** always flows in the same direction, from a fixed positive terminal to the fixed negative terminal of a supply.

A typical d.c. circuit is shown in the figure on the right. A cell or battery gives a constant (steady) direct current. A graph of voltage versus time for a d.c. supply is shown in the figure below. The current is described as being **unidirectional**.

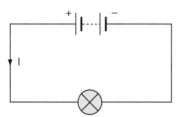

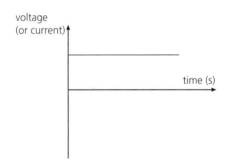

The electricity supply to your home is an **alternating current (a.c.)** supply. In an a.c. supply, the voltage (and hence the current) changes size and direction in a regular and repetitive way, as shown by the graph opposite. In fact, the mains voltage on the live wire changes from +325 V to −325 V. The average value of this voltage is 230 V. The voltage on the neutral wire is **0 volts at all times**. The current changes direction 100 times every second and makes 50 complete cycles per second – hence the frequency of the mains is 50 Hz.

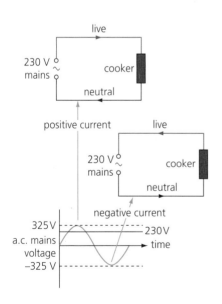

An a.c. supply is said to be **bidirectional**.

> **Exam tip**
> A common mistake is to write that a.c. flows in **both** directions. It doesn't. It always flows from high voltage to low voltage. Alternating current flows in one direction and then in the opposite direction regularly.

1 a) A colour television is marked 240 V, 80 W.

    i) Explain fully what these numbers mean.   **[2 marks]**

    ii) Calculate the current that passes through this appliance when it is on.   **[3 marks]**

    iii) Select a fuse that should be fitted to this appliance from the list: 1 A, 3 A, 5 A, 13 A Explain your choice.   **[2 marks]**

    iv) Calculate the resistance of this television set.   **[3 marks]**

    v) The flex that connects this television to the mains has only two wires inside it. The diagram below shows the inside of a three-pin plug. Copy and complete the diagram to show how the plug should be wired. Label each wire with its name and colour.

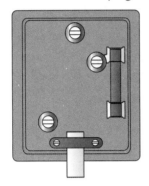

    [3 marks]

    vi) To which of these wires should the switch on the television be connected?   **[1 mark]**

    vii) Apart from allowing the user to switch the television on and off, this is done for another reason. What is this other reason?   **[1 mark]**

    viii) Explain how the owner of the television is protected from possible electrical shock.

    [3 marks]

b) The oven of an electric cooker is rated at 8 kW. Calculate the cost of using the oven to cook for 2 hours. The cost of electricity is 11p per unit.   **[3 marks]**

2 The diagram below shows a typical situation in a house. The landing light is operated by switches at the top and at the bottom of the stairs, each being able to switch the light on or off as desired.

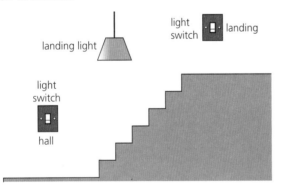

Complete the wiring diagram below for this situation.

mains
o ~ o

switch

switch

    [4 marks]

3 a) Explain fully how the various wires and other components within a three-pin plug protect the user from electric shock should a fault occur in an electric motor. The motor has a metal case. In this question you will be assessed on your written communication skills, including the use of specialist science terms.   **[6 marks]**

b) To test the wiring of a three-pin plug connected to a metal kettle, the equipment shown below was set up.

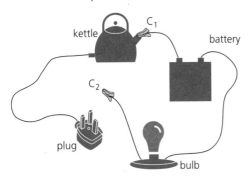

C_1 and C_2 are metal clips. C_1 is connected to the metal body of the kettle. When clip C_2 is connected to the earth pin of the three-pin plug, describe what should be observed if the wiring of the plug is correct. Explain your answer.   **[3 marks]**

Go online for the answers   Online

13 Magnetism

A **bar magnet** has two poles called north and south. Around every bar magnet is a magnetic field where other magnetic materials experience a force. The shape of the magnetic field is shown by **field lines**, which always point away from the north pole and towards the south pole. Field lines must **never** cross or touch. The closer the lines are, the stronger the magnetic field is.

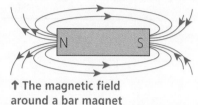

↑ **The magnetic field around a bar magnet**

Bar magnets are called **permanent magnets** because their magnetism cannot be switched on and off. Even if stored in a drawer for decades, they retain their magnetism. They are usually made of steel.

You need to know how to find the shape of the magnetic field around a bar magnet using **plotting compasses**.

Plotting field lines around a bar magnet

1   A plotting compass is a small, suspended magnet enclosed in an aluminium case with a glass window. It will come to rest pointing along a magnetic field line.

2   Place the magnet on a sheet of white paper and draw its outline.

3   Place the plotting compass near the north pole and, with a pencil, place a dot on the paper where the needle is pointing.

4   Move the compass so that the dot is directly below the tail of the compass needle. Mark a new dot at the head of the needle.

5   Continue moving the compass in this way until you reach the magnet or the edge of the paper.

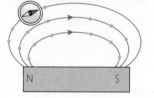

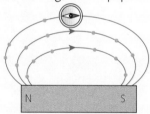

6   Starting at different points near the north pole, repeat this procedure until several field lines have been drawn.

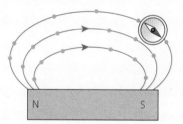

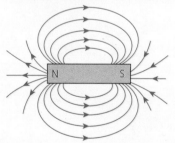

> **Exam tip**
>
> Remember that around a bar magnet, field lines always point away from a north pole and towards a south pole.

A similar procedure to that described for a bar magnet is used to find the magnetic field pattern around a long, straight wire or a coil carrying an electric current.

Magnetic field around a coil carrying an electric current

We can produce a much larger magnetic field by wrapping the wire in the form of a long, straight coil. This is called a **solenoid**. The magnetic field strength can be increased by:

- using a larger current
- using more turns of wire
- putting a soft iron rod into the solenoid.

The direction of the magnetic field can be found by looking **end-on** at the solenoid. If the current flows clockwise then that end is south; if the current flows anticlockwise then that end is north.

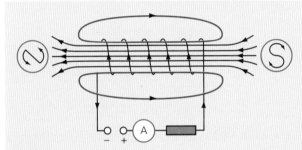

The motor effect

- A current-carrying wire placed inside a magnetic field generally experiences a force.

- The direction of the force is perpendicular to both the field lines and the current. Reversing the direction of the current (or the field) will reverse the direction of the force.

- The size of the force is greatest when the current is perpendicular to the field lines and zero when the current is parallel to the field lines.

- The effect is known as the motor effect and is used in an electric motor.

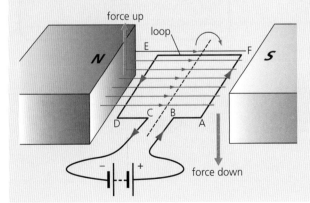

Note that there is no force on sides EF and DA, because the current here is parallel to the magnetic field lines. The force on side AF is vertically downwards and the force on side DE is vertically upwards in accordance with **Fleming's Left Hand Rule**.

The force arises from the interaction of the field from the current (circular field) and the field from the permanent magnet (linear). The direction of the force on the conductor is given by Fleming's Left Hand Rule. Only Higher Tier GCSE Physics (but not DAS) candidates must be able to apply Fleming's Left Hand Rule. The rule is illustrated below.

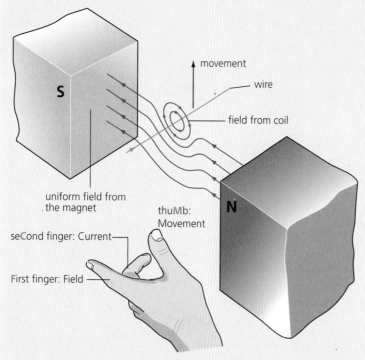

Ensure the thumb and first two fingers of the left hand are held at right-angles to each other.

- Make the first finger point in the direction of the field.
- Make the second finger point in the direction of the current.
- Then the thumb will point in the direction of the force or motion.

When applying this rule, remember:

- The field direction is from the north pole of a magnet to the south pole.
- The current direction is from the positive terminal of a battery round to the negative.

The electric motor

When the coil is horizontal the forces on the side arms of the coil are vertical, in opposite directions and at their maximum. The coil eventually reaches a vertical position and momentarily there is no current and no turning force whatsoever. As the coil overshoots this vertical position, the commutator reverses the direction of the current in the coil so that it continues to rotate in the same direction as before. In this way the coil continues to rotate clockwise.

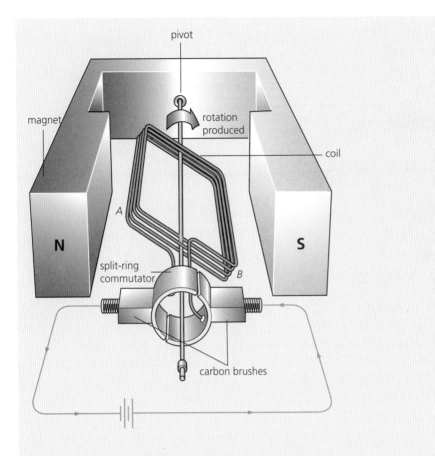

The turning effect on the coil can be increased by:

● increasing the current in the coil

● increasing the strength of the magnetic field

● increasing the number of turns on the coil

● increasing the area of the coil

Note that reversing the polarity of the magnet or the direction of the current (by reversing the battery polarity) will reverse the direction in which the coil rotates.

Electromagnetic induction
Revised

In an electric motor the user supplies an **electric current** and a **magnetic field** to produce **motion**.

In **electromagnetic induction** the user supplies a **magnetic field** and **motion** to produce an **electric current**.

The diagram on the next page shows an early induction experiment. When the wire is pulled up or down through the field (in the XX' direction) in such a way as to 'cut' field lines, an induced current is detected on the sensitive ammeter. If the wire moves but no field lines are cut (in directions YY' or ZZ'), then there is no induced current. Reversing the direction of movement of the wire reverses the current direction.

The size of the induced current can be increased by:

● moving the wire faster

● using a stronger magnet

● looping the wire so that several turns pass through the poles.

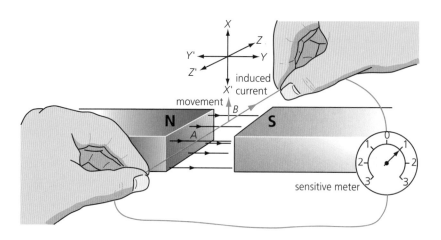

Current induction in stationary wire

A current can also be induced in a stationary wire, usually a coil, by moving a magnetic field as illustrated below.

As the magnet is being moved into (or out of) the coil, a current is observed on the ammeter. Once the magnet stops moving there is no longer an induced current – so the deflection on the needle on the meter is only **momentary**. Reversing the direction of its motion or the polarity of the magnet reverses the direction of the induced current. This current reversal can be detected on the centre-zero ammeter.

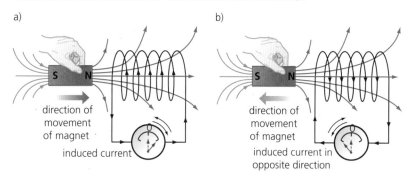

a)

direction of
movement
of magnet

induced current

b)

direction of
movement
of magnet

induced current in
opposite direction

There are two major applications of electromagnetic induction – the **a.c. generator** and the **transformer**.

Current induction using two coils

The third way to induce a current is to change a current in one of two neighbouring coils. Two coils are wrapped on an iron ring. One coil is connected to a switch and battery, while the other is connected to a centre-zero ammeter to detect electric current and show its direction.

● **When the switch is closed** there is an **increase** in the current in the primary coil, which induces a **momentary current** in the secondary coil.

● When a steady current flows in the primary coil, there is **no current** in the secondary coil.

● **As the switch is opened**, there is a **momentary current** in the primary coil, but this time in the **opposite direction.**

The **iron ring** shown in the diagram magnifies the effect, but is not absolutely essential.

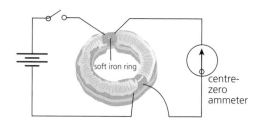

soft iron ring

centre-
zero
ammeter

The a.c. generator

Part a) of the figure here shows the design of a very simple alternating current (a.c.) generator. It consists of a rectangular coil that can rotate about an axle between the poles of a magnet. The ends of the coil are attached to slip rings against which carbon brushes press.

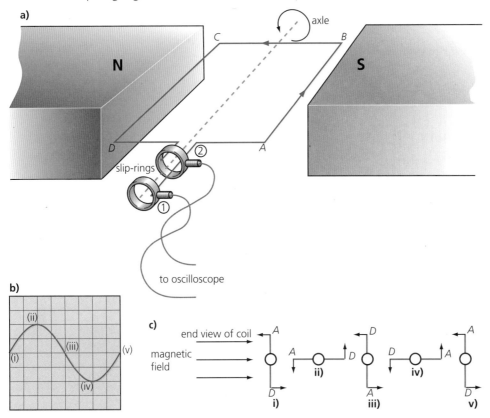

a)

b)

c)

When the axle is turned, a coil of wire moves through a magnetic field. This induces a voltage between the ends of the coil.

Part b) of the figure shows how the voltage waveform produced by the generator looks on an oscilloscope screen. Parts b) and c) together match the various positions of the coil with the output voltage. The **frequency of the output voltage** is the same as the frequency of rotation of the coil.

A.c. and d.c.

The generator described above produces a current that is constantly changing its direction. We call this **alternating current (a.c.)**. Current that always flows in the same direction is called **direct current (d.c.)**. Batteries provide d.c., whereas generators and some laboratory power supply units provide a.c. Alternating current signals, when represented on a graph, must cross the time axis – this indicates a reversal of direction. Direct current signals must not.

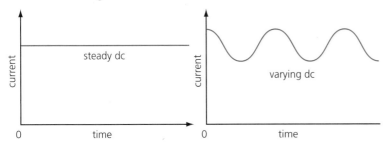

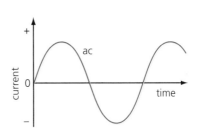

Transformers

A transformer changes an alternating voltage from one value to another. It consists of two coils of insulated wire wrapped around an iron core. The input voltage is connected to the primary coil and the output voltage is taken from the secondary coil.

Step-up transformers increase the voltage – they have more turns on the secondary coil than the primary coil (part **a**) of the figure below).

Step-down transformers decrease the voltage – they have more turns on the primary coil than the secondary (part **b**) of the figure below).

Part **c**) of the figure shows the symbol for a transformer.

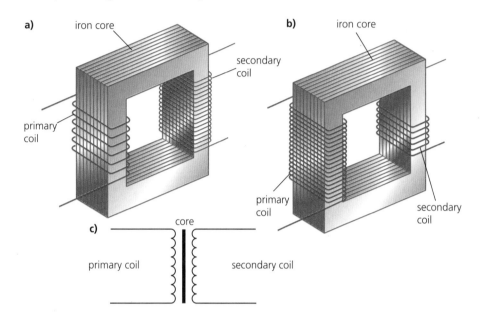

The voltages at the primary and secondary coils are related to each other through the **turns ratio transformer equation:**

$$\frac{N_s}{N_p} = \frac{V_s}{V_p}$$

Exam tip

This equation must be memorised.

N_s is the number of turns on the secondary coil

N_p is the number of turns on the primary coil

V_s is the voltage at the secondary coil

V_p is the voltage at the primary coil

Transformers are very efficient devices and (at GCSE) we can assume there is no wasted energy at all. We can therefore write:

power in = $V_p I_p = V_s I_s$ = power out

Exam tip

This is simply an application of Joule's law. Although there is no reference to the above equation in the specification, examiners may set questions that require you to recall Joule's law and apply it to a transformer.

Electricity transmission

A typical generator at a power station might produce a current of 22 000 A at a voltage of 25 000 V.

● Before transfer to the overhead power lines, the generator's output is passed to a **large step-up transformer** to raise the voltage to about 275 000 V and reduce the current to about 2000 A.

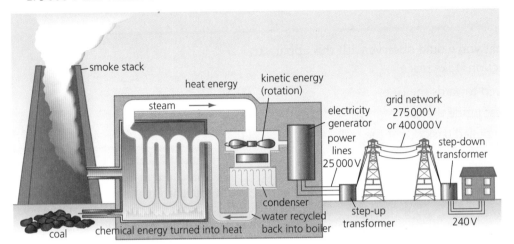

● The overhead power cables transmit this electrical energy all over the country in a network known as the **National Grid**. Power from the Grid is then distributed to customers after the voltage is reduced in stages in **step-down transformers** at electricity substations to much safer levels.

● **High voltage transmission** means that a **smaller current** can be used to transmit a given amount of power.

● A low current means that there is **less energy lost** in the cables as heat and the cables need not be so thick.

● Less heat loss saves energy and conserves fossil fuels at the power stations.

Worked example 1

1   A coil of wire is connected to a sensitive ammeter.

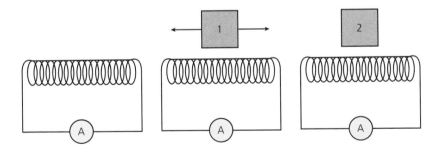

    a) When box 1 is moving beside the coil, a current is induced in the coil. Suggest what box 1 contains.   **[1]**

    b) When box 2 is stationary beside the coil, a current is induced in the coil. Suggest what box 2 contains.   **[1]**

2   A transformer in a phone charger is needed to step down the voltage from 240 V to 9 V. The secondary coil has 180 turns. How many turns are on the primary coil?   **[4]**

3   The diagram below shows a wire coil and a strong magnet. The coil is connected to a sensitive ammeter that has a zero at the centre of its scale.

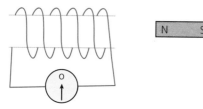

Describe carefully what you would observe with this apparatus when the following actions take place.

a) The magnet is moved towards the coil.   [2]
b) The magnet is at rest inside the coil.   [1]
c) The magnet is then pulled back out of the coil.   [3]

Answers

1   a) A permanent magnet

     b) An alternating current flowing in a wire/coil of wire. (An alternative acceptable answer is that there is **a spinning magnet** in Box 2.)

Exam tip

This question requires careful thought. Box 1 is moving – so what is needed to provide a changing magnetic field at the coil? Box 2 is stationary, so what do we need inside box 2 to provide a changing magnetic field at the coil?

2    $V_s = 9\,V$, $V_p = 240\,V$ and $N_s = 180$ turns
Applying the turns-ratio equation:

$$\frac{N_s}{N_p} = \frac{V_s}{V_p}$$

So, substituting gives $\dfrac{180}{N_p} = \dfrac{9}{240}$

and rearranging gives $N_p = \dfrac{180 \times 240}{9} = 4800$ turns

Exam tip

This is a straightforward question that shows how important it is to learn equations and how to apply them. Writing down the wrong equation would almost certainly lead to scoring no marks whatsoever.

3   a) The needle deflects and then returns to zero.
     b) The needle remains at rest – there is no deflection.
     c) The needle momentarily deflects, but in the opposite direction to in **a)**, and then returns to zero.

Revision Questions   Tested

1   The charger of a mobile phone is plugged into a 240 V mains supply. It must deliver only 4 V to charge the battery of the mobile phone.

     a) The power output of the charger is 120 mW. Calculate the current it supplies in milliamperes.   [4 marks]

     b) If the primary (input) coil of the charger has 18 000 turns, how many turns must be on the secondary (output) coil?   [4 marks]

2 The block diagram below shows the main stages in the transmission of electricity.

generator → transformer A → Grid → transformer B → customer

a) What types of transformer are A and B? [2 marks]

b) Explain in detail why transformers A and B are needed. [4 marks]

c) The diagram below shows an a.c. generator.

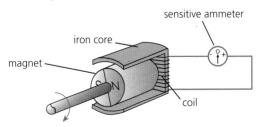

sensitive ammeter

iron core

magnet

coil

i) What happens in the coil of wire when the magnet rotates? [1 mark]

ii) What name is given to this effect? [1 mark]

The sensitive ammeter is removed and the ends of the coil are connected to a cathode ray oscilloscope (CRO).

iii) Draw the trace that might be seen on the CRO. [2 marks]

iv) How is the output from this a.c. generator different from that obtained from a battery? [3 marks]

3 The diagram below shows the layout of a power pack that is found in most schools. The power pack contains a transformer. There is a moveable switch that can be turned so it touches the contacts A to K. This allows the output voltage (secondary voltage) to be varied.

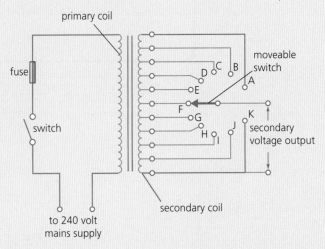

primary coil

fuse

switch

to 240 volt mains supply

secondary coil

moveable switch

A B C D E F G H I J K

secondary voltage output

a) The input primary voltage is 240 V. The maximum value of the output voltage is 20 V. The primary coil has 6000 turns of wire. Calculate the number of turns on the secondary coil.

[3 marks]

b) There are 50 turns of wire between consecutive pairs of terminals A to K, i.e. between A and B there are 50 turns, between B and C there are 50 turns, and so on. In what voltage steps can the secondary voltage output be varied? [3 marks]

Go online for the answers — Online

14 The Solar System

The Earth is one of eight planets that orbit a star we call the Sun. Listed in order of distance from the Sun, the planets are:

Mercury, Venus, Earth, Mars, Jupiter, Saturn, Uranus and **Neptune.**

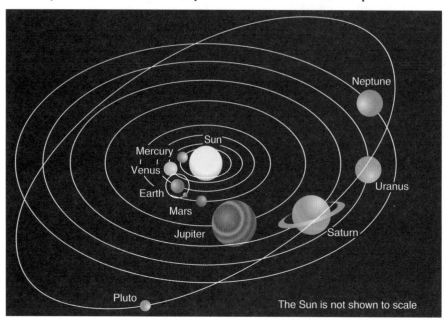

↑ The Solar System

All the planets orbit the Sun in **elliptical** paths.

The Sun and all the objects that orbit it – planets, moons, asteroids and comets – are called the **Solar System**.

In 2006 Pluto was re-classified as a 'dwarf planet' and examiners now expect you to know that **Pluto is not a planet**.

- **Moons** are natural satellites of planets. This means that moons orbit planets, just as the planets orbit the Sun.

- **Asteroids** are lumps of rock, ranging in size from 1 km to 1000 km across. Most orbit the Sun in a 'belt' between Mars and Jupiter. Sometimes they can be thrown out of orbit and pass near the Earth.

- **Comets** are made up of ice and dust. They travel around the Sun in very elongated (eccentric) orbits. This means that sometimes they are very close to the Sun and occasionally visible from Earth, and sometimes they are very far away – far beyond Pluto. The comet's head is the cloud-like mass we see in the front. The tail is the trailing part, pointing away from the Sun, and is made up of small particles and ice.

> **Exam tip**
>
> A mnemonic to help you remember the eight planets is:
>
> My Very Easy Method Just Sums Up Nothing!
>
> Better still – make your own!

Heliocentric or geocentric?

Revised

The structure of the Solar System just described is that proposed by the **heliocentric theory** because it places the Sun at the centre ('helios' is Greek for Sun). However, from about 500BC to the mid-17th century, people believed in the **geocentric theory**, which placed the **Earth at the centre of the Universe** ('ge' is Greek for Earth). They believed that the Moon, Mercury, Venus, the Sun, Mars, Jupiter, Saturn and the stars all moved around the Earth in **circular** (not elliptical) **paths**.

At that time only six of the eight planets were known, because Uranus and Neptune cannot be seen without a telescope. The geocentric theory had three major problems, which it could not readily explain.

● The strange looping motion (retrograde motion) of Jupiter and Saturn.

● The phases (changing crescent-shaped appearances) of Mercury and Venus.

● The apparent changes in the brightness of Venus and of Mars.

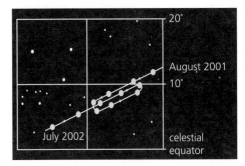

↑ **Retrograde (looping) motion of Jupiter**

A Greek astronomer called Ptolemy put forward a **theory of epicycles** to explain Jupiter's loops. Ptolemy believed that Jupiter moved in a circular path (the small circle below) around a point that orbited the Earth (on the big circle). This, he proposed, caused the planet's path to appear (from Earth) to loop back on itself as it traversed the sky.

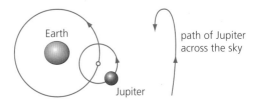

Around 1515, Nicolas Copernicus put forward the new **heliocentric theory**, with all the planets orbiting the Sun in circular orbits. This challenged the teaching of the Church that God had put the Earth at the centre of the Universe. At that time the Church was very powerful and Copernicus' ideas were not accepted.

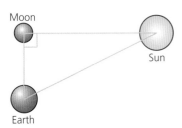

In the 1580s Tycho Brahe, using a sextant (telescopes had not been invented), showed that the Sun, Moon and Earth at times formed a right-angled triangle, with the Sun–Earth as the hypotenuse. So at times the Sun was further from the Earth than from the Moon, contrary to the geocentric theory.

It was not until 1610 and the invention of the telescope that better observation of the planets was possible. This allowed Johannes Kepler to collect a lot of data and show convincingly that the planets all move in elliptical paths around the Sun, and to provide explanations for all the observations listed at the top of this page. The epicycle ideas were shown to be nonsense. Gradually the heliocentric theory gained approval and today it is universally accepted.

Newton and gravity

In the mid-17th century, Isaac Newton was asking himself what force caused the planets to orbit the Sun. His explanation was that **any two masses in the Universe attract each other**, just as the opposite poles of a magnet attract each other.

This **gravitational force:**

● increases with the masses of the objects

● decreases the further they are apart

● acts along the line joining their centres of mass.

In the diagram below the five large planets all have the same mass, which is larger than that of the small planet. The distances are to scale. The force F_A is the biggest (largest masses, closest together) and the force F_B is the smallest (one small mass and as far apart as in C).

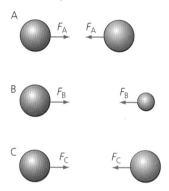

Gravitational forces only become important when at least one of the masses is **very large**, like a planet or a star or a galaxy. **Gravity** provides the **centripetal force** for the **orbital motion** of the planets, asteroids and comets around the Sun, for the moons round the planets, and for artificial satellites around the Earth.

Notice that **gravitational forces come in pairs,** acting between the centres of mass. The force on a book pulling it towards the centre of mass of the Earth is exactly the same size as the force on the Earth pulling it towards the book. But the mass of the book is much less than that of the Earth, so the effect of the force on the book is much greater.

Artificial satellites

The Moon is a **natural satellite** of the Earth. Since the late 1950s, people have put **artificial satellites** into orbit around the Earth. They are used mainly for:

● astronomy (for example the Hubble Telescope)

● communications (long-distance phone calls and radio/TV broadcasts)

● weather monitoring/forecasting

● monitoring agricultural land use

● monitoring military activity, and general espionage.

The complex electronic equipment in an artificial satellite needs electrical energy. Often it gets this by deploying large arrays of photocells, which convert the light energy of the Sun into electrical energy. However, the satellite does not generally need energy to maintain its motion. This is because it is well above the atmosphere and so there is no friction force opposing its motion.

Worked example 1

The diagram shows the Earth and two of its artificial satellites.

a) Draw an arrow from satellite A to show the direction of the gravitational force acting on it due to the Earth. **[1]**

b) The table below gives some data on the two satellites.

Satellite	Mass (kilograms)	Orbital radius (kilometres)
A	8000	600
B	5000	30 000

i) Which of the two satellites experiences the larger gravitational force? **[1]**

ii) Explain your answer to **b) i)**. **[2]**

Answers

a) An arrow should be drawn from the centre of A towards the centre of the Earth (but not beyond it).

b) i) A

ii) A has a greater mass than B, and gravitational force increases with mass. A is also nearer the centre of the Earth than B, and gravitational force increases as the distance between the masses decreases.

Geostationary satellites

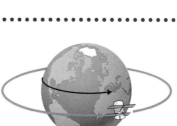

These can also be called **geosynchronous** satellites. They are placed about 36 000 km above the Equator and take exactly 24 hours to orbit the Earth. The Earth also takes 24 hours to spin on its axis. So, to an observer on the Earth these satellites appear to be standing still – hence the name 'geostationary'. The satellites must:

● orbit in the equatorial plane

● orbit the Earth in the same direction as the Earth spins on its axis.

Geosynchronous satellites are ideal for:

● telephone, microwave (mobile telephone) and TV communications

● global positioning systems (for use in SatNavs).

Low polar orbit satellites

In a low polar orbit, the satellite sweeps over both poles while the Earth rotates beneath it. The time taken for each full orbit of the satellite is just a few hours. Each time the satellite comes round it can **scan** a **different part** of the Earth. This means that the whole surface of the planet can be monitored each day.

Satellites in low polar orbits are ideal for:

● taking photographs for weather forecasting

● spying on military installations

● monitoring movements in the ice sheets at the North and South Poles.

Satellites in astronomy

A big advantage of astronomical telescopes on satellites (like the Hubble Telescope) is that they can:

- take photographs without the blurring caused by the Earth's atmosphere
- view stars, planets and galaxies in greater detail
- take photographs in the X-ray, ultraviolet, infrared and radio wave parts of the spectrum.

The galaxies — Revised

- Our **Solar System** contains only one star – the **Sun**.
- But as we look into the night sky we see a vast number of star systems.
- These make up our galaxy, the **Milky Way**.
- A typical galaxy contains around a billion stars.
- The Universe is thought to contain over a hundred billion galaxies.

Stars — Revised

- Most stars are composed mainly of **hydrogen** and **helium**.
- The **hydrogen** gas at a star's centre exists in the form of **nuclei**, not atoms or molecules.
- These nuclei are **positively charged** and therefore tend to **repel** each other.
- The temperature at the centre of a typical star is very high (more than 15 million degrees).
- So the hydrogen nuclei are moving at enormous speeds.
- When they collide, they can form a new, heavier nucleus (helium).
- This is **nuclear fusion** and it causes the release of vast quantities of **energy** (electromagnetic radiation).

How are stars formed?

- A star is formed from clouds of hydrogen and dust, known as a **stellar nebula**.
- Particles of hydrogen come together because of **gravity**.
- These clouds become more and more **dense** as the particles get closer and closer together.
- Hydrogen particles start to **spiral inwards** and the temperature rises enormously.
- The temperature reaches about **15 million °C**.
- At this temperature, **nuclear fusion** begins and a star is born.

You should appreciate that gravitation is responsible for the forces between all of the heavenly bodies. New stars, new galaxies and new planets are continually being created due to gravity.

How are planets formed?

Revised

- The remaining clouds of gas and dust are called a **planetary nebula**.
- They clump together due to **gravity** in a process called **accretion**.
- Over a very **long period** of time they become planets.
- The presence of a massive star may cause them to become **trapped in its orbit**.
- Since the gas and dust clouds originally spiralled in the same direction, so the planets would orbit that star in the **same sense** (all clockwise or all anticlockwise) and in the **same plane**.

Why are the four inner planets rocky and the four outer planets gaseous?

As the Sun began to shine, its radiation 'blew' much of the gas away to the outer reaches of the Solar System. Here the gas collected by gravitation to form the outer planets (Jupiter, Saturn, Uranus and Neptune). However, the dust particles, being of greater mass, were not 'blown' so far and, over millions of years, gravitational accretion caused the dust to form the inner, rocky planets (Mercury, Venus, Earth and Mars).

Solar stability

Revised

- The Sun is converting mass into energy at a rate of about 4 million tonnes per second.
- But its apparent size in the sky has remained the same for as long as humankind has been on Earth.
- This is because the force of gravity, which pulls inwards towards the centre, exactly balances the outward force (called radiation 'pressure') due to the thermonuclear explosions.

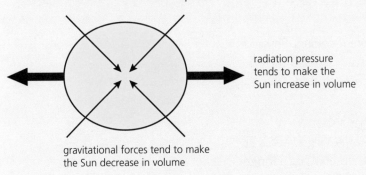

radiation pressure
tends to make the
Sun increase in volume

gravitational forces tend to make
the Sun decrease in volume

Formation and evolution of the Universe

Revised

- Most physicists today accept the **Big Bang Theory** as the best model to describe the origin of the Universe.
- The Big Bang occurred between **12 000 and 15 000 million years ago** from a tiny point that physicists call a **singularity**. It was not an explosion of the conventional type, because it was only then that matter, energy and time came into existence.

- Not long after the Big Bang, the Universe was made up of high-energy radiation and elementary particles like quarks, the particles that make up protons and neutrons. This was a period of rapid expansion or 'inflation'.

- Rapid expansion is always associated with cooling, so as the Universe got bigger it cooled down. This allowed the quarks to come together to form protons and neutrons.

- Further expansion and cooling allowed the temperature to fall sufficiently to enable electrons to combine with neutrons and protons to form atoms of hydrogen.

Red-shift

If a source of waves is moving, the crests of its waves get bunched together in front of the wave source. If the wave crests are bunched together, their wavelength decreases.

On the other side of the source (behind it), the waves spread out and the wavelength increases.

 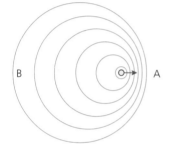

source of sound at rest — source of sound moving to the right

This is why the sound of a siren from an emergency vehicle appears to have a higher pitch (smaller wavelength) as it approaches us and a lower pitch (bigger wavelength) as it moves away from us. This is called the Doppler efect.

Visible light consists of much more than seven different colours. Physicists prefer to think that there is a continuum from red to violet – so there are an infinite number of colours in the visible spectrum. Each colour has a wavelength associated with it.

If the light that we observe from a moving source has a shorter wavelength than expected, it is because the source is moving towards us – we say the light is 'blue-shifted'. But if the light we observe has a **longer wavelength** than expected, it is because the **source is moving away** from us – and we say the light is **'red-shifted'**.

Our Sun contains hydrogen. We know this because there are black lines in the spectrum of the light from the Sun, where hydrogen atoms have absorbed light. This pattern of black lines is called the **absorption spectrum** for hydrogen.

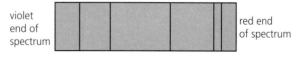

violet end of spectrum — red end of spectrum

By closely examining the light spectrum, physicists have identified over 50 different elements in the Sun.

What happens when we look at the light from distant galaxies?

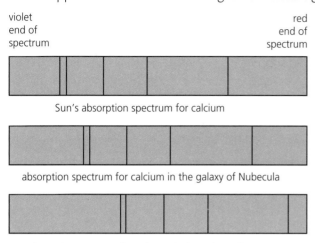

violet
end of
spectrum

red
end of
spectrum

Sun's absorption spectrum for calcium

absorption spectrum for calcium in the galaxy of Nubecula

absorption spectrum for calcium in the galaxy of Leo

↑ **These spectra demonstrate red-shift and show that both Nubecula and Leo are moving away from us.**

- We get the same pattern as we do from the Sun but it is shifted **towards** the **red end** of the spectrum.

- The fact that we always get **red-shift** from the distant galaxies tells us that the galaxies are all moving away from us.

- This tells us that the **Universe is expanding** – the distance between the galaxies is getting bigger and bigger.

An expanding Universe supports the Big Bang Theory.

> **Exam tip**
> Remember that red-shift involves an increase in the wavelength of light from distant GALAXIES (not stars)!

Cosmic microwave background radiation

- In the 1960s two American physicists, Arno Penzias and Bob Wilson, discovered microwaves coming from all parts of the sky.

- Today most physicists believe that this continuous, **cosmic microwave background radiation (CMBR)** is the remnant or 'echo' of the Big Bang.

- The CMBR corresponds to the radiation emitted by a black body at a temperature of about −270°C or 3 Kelvin. It is sometimes called 3 K continuous background radiation.

- The existence of this CMBR is further evidence of the Big Bang.

- The Big Bang Theory is currently the only model that explains CMBR.

What will happen to the Universe in the future?

Whether or not the Universe keeps on expanding depends on the amount of matter there is. The different possible scenarios are:

- **Big Freeze:** if there is too little mass, the Universe will expand forever and get colder and colder, ending in a Big Freeze.

- **Big Crunch:** if there is enough mass in the Universe, gravitational forces will cause the expansion to eventually stop. Contraction will then start, galaxies will move towards each other and collide, and the Universe will end in a Big Crunch.

- **Big Bounce:** some physicists have suggested that gravity may be big enough to bring matter so close together that conditions will be similar to those not long after the Big Bang. If further contraction occurs, the Universe may collapse to another singularity and another Big Bang can occur. According to this idea, the Universe is destined to repeatedly crunch, bang, crunch and so on.

By the end of 2011, over 700 planets outside our Solar System had been discovered. Of course, it is not known if any of these planets can support life as we know it.

How are planets outside our Solar System detected? This is often done by observing the light coming from stars that are similar to our Sun. Astronomers look for a 'transition' – a tiny reduction in the light reaching us from that star when an orbiting planet passes between the star and us.

Space travel within our Solar System

- People first set foot on the surface of the Moon in 1969 and, so far, humans have never ventured further than the Moon.
- On 15 April 2010 the US President said: 'By the mid-2030s, I believe we can send humans to orbit Mars and return them safely to Earth. And a landing on Mars will follow.'

Space travel beyond the Solar System

- Our fastest spacecraft can travel at a maximum speed of 70 000 m/s.
- At this speed it would take a staggering 18 000 years to reach the nearest planet outside the Solar System.
- The vast distances to the stars mean that it is certain that with our present technology it is not feasible to visit any planet outside our Solar System.

There are enormous difficulties:

- **Flight time** – the distance is so great that the flight would last for many generations.
- **Engineering** – our spacecraft are just too slow.
- **Logistics** – it is not clear how the spacecraft could carry enough fuel, oxygen and water.
- **Ethical** – the chance of failure would be high, with no possibility of return to Earth.

Search for extra-terrestrial intelligence

If there is life on other planets, we are most likely to detect it using large arrays of radio telescopes. How do scientists carry out the search for extra-terrestrial intelligence (SETI)? Broadly speaking, they look for non-random radio signals coming from distant star systems – it is rather like trying to pick up EastEnders from space!

1 Write the following objects in order of increasing size:
   star   planet   asteroid   galaxy   Universe   [1 mark]

2 **a)** What is 'red-shift'?   [2 marks]

   b) What does red-shift tell us about neighbouring galaxies?   [1 mark]

3 List the planets in order as you travel away from the Sun.   [1 mark]

4 What does the Big Bang Theory have to say about the origin of the Universe?   [2 marks]

5 What is nuclear fusion and where does it occur in the Universe?   [2 marks]

6 How did the planets come into existence?   [2 marks]

7 **a)** The diagram here shows the Sun.

Sun

   Redraw the diagram carefully and label the path:
   i) a planet would take   [1 mark]
   ii) a moon would take.   [1 mark]

   b) State **one** property of the motion of the planets that suggests our Solar System was formed from a gas cloud (nebula).   [1 mark]

   c) Observations of light from the stars in distant galaxies tell us that the galaxies are moving away; in other words space is expanding. How do we know from observations that a galaxy is moving away from us?   [2 marks]

   d) The table below gives some information on distances to some of our closest galaxies and the speed with which they are moving away. Our own galaxy, the Milky Way, is included in the table.

Galaxy	Distance from Milky Way in millions of light years	Speed in km/s
Milky Way (our galaxy)	0	0
Virgo	80	1200
Perseus	350	5400
Hercules	650	10 000
Ursa Major	1000	15 000

   i) The astronomer Edwin Hubble, in a law named after him, proposed that the speed of the galaxy v and the distance d to the galaxy are related by the equation: $v = Hd$

   where H is a constant known as Hubble's constant.

   To test the validity of Hubble's law a graph can be drawn.

   What quantities would you plot on the x-axis and on the y-axis?   [2 marks]

   ii) Using the measurements in the table, draw a graph to test the validity of Hubble's law.   [4 marks]

   iii) Does the graph validate Hubble's law? Explain your answer.   [3 marks]

8   Photographs from the Hubble Telescope show distant objects in the Universe. Some of them are spinning gas clouds.

    a) i) Give another name for a gas cloud.   **[1 mark]**

       ii) What does the spinning gas cloud consist of?   **[2 marks]**

      iii) What happens gradually to the material in the spinning gas cloud as time passes?   **[3 marks]**

      iv) What will eventually be formed in the spinning gas cloud after millions of years?   **[1 mark]**

    b) i) Name the nuclear process that powers a star.   **[1 mark]**

       ii) Name one type of energy produced by this nuclear process.   **[1 mark]**

9   The Solar System forms part of a galaxy. The galaxy is part of a larger system.

    a) What is the name of the larger system?   **[1 mark]**

    b) The diagram below shows the eight planets that orbit the Sun.

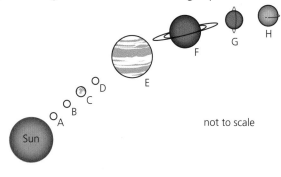

not to scale

      i) Name the planet that is furthest from the Sun.   **[1 mark]**

      Use the letters A to G to answer the following two questions.

      ii) Which planet is the Earth?   **[1 mark]**

     iii) Between which planets would you encounter most asteroids?   **[1 mark]**

     iv) Name the four giant planets – E, F, G and H.   **[2 marks]**

    c) The Sun emits radiation. What nuclear process takes place in the Sun to enable it to emit radiation?   **[1 mark]**

    d) Man has visited the Moon on several occasions. Explain fully why no one has visited Mars, which is much further away.   **[2 marks]**

10 The light from the stars in galaxies other than our own is observed to be red-shifted.

    a) What is meant by red-shift?   **[1 mark]**

    b) What does red-shift tell us about the motion of these galaxies?   **[1 mark]**

    c) What is Cosmic Microwave Background Radiation and what is its significance?   **[2 marks]**

Go online for the answers ────────────────────── Online

15 The Structure of the Earth

- The Earth has an 'onion' structure consisting of four layers – a solid outer **crust** floats on a thick, viscous **mantle**, while a liquid **outer core** surrounds a dense, solid **inner core**.

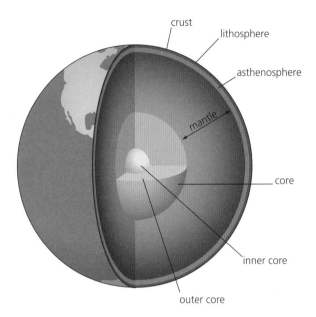

- The crust is very thin – about 20 km or so on average – and is mainly **basalt rock**.
- The mantle lies below the crust and is around 2900 km thick. It consists mainly of **silica and minerals** of iron, magnesium and other metals.
- The Earth's **lithosphere** is the **crust and the upper, solid part of the upper mantle**.
- The core is mainly **iron** and **nickel**.
- By following the paths of earthquake waves as they travel through the Earth, we can tell that there is a change from solid to liquid about halfway through the Earth. This is why we believe that the outer core is liquid.
- **Earthquake waves** also indicate that the Earth has a solid inner core.

It is now generally believed that it is **radioactive decay** that creates all the heat inside the Earth. This heat causes the convection currents, which cause the plates of the crust to move.

Plate tectonics

- The Earth's lithosphere is the crust and the upper part of the mantle.
- It is cracked into pieces called **tectonic plates**.
- The word 'tectonic' simply means 'within the crust of the Earth'.
- These plates are like big rafts. The diagram on the next page shows the edges of these plates.
- As they move, the continents move too.
- The plates are moving very slowly, at a speed of about 1 or 2 cm per year.

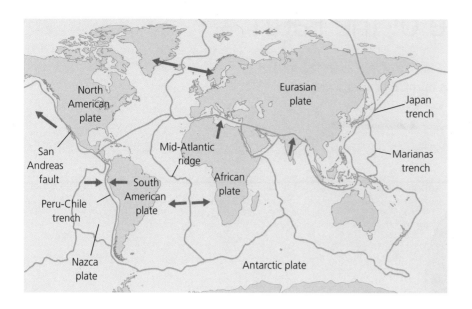

Plate boundaries

At the **boundaries between tectonic plates** there is usually **volcanic and/or earthquake activity**. This can be explained in terms of the movement of the plates. There are three different ways that plates interact – sliding past each other, colliding or separating.

Plates sliding past each other

- Sometimes, plates just slide past each other.

- The best known example of this is the San Andreas Fault in California (see diagram opposite).

- A narrow strip of the coastline (along the edge of the Nazca plate) is sliding north while the North American plate is sliding south.

- Big plates of rock don't glide past each other smoothly – they catch on each other and as the **pressure builds up** they can **suddenly lurch** and cause an **earthquake**.

- This sudden lurching lasts only a few seconds – but it can bring buildings down.

- In earthquake zones they try to build earthquake-proof buildings that are designed to withstand a bit of shaking.

- Earthquakes usually cause much greater devastation in poorer countries where there may be overcrowded cities, poorly constructed buildings and inadequate rescue services.

Oceanic and continental plates colliding

What happens when an oceanic and a continental plate collide?

- The oceanic plate is less dense and is always forced underneath the continental plate, as in the diagram on the next page.

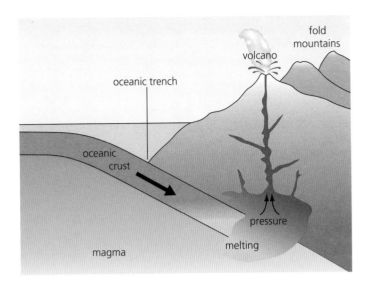

- As the oceanic crust is pushed down, friction causes the rocks to melt.
- The molten rock is forced to the surface and volcanoes form.
- There can also be earthquakes as the two plates slowly grind past each other.
- A **deep trench** forms on the ocean floor where the oceanic plate is being forced down.
- The continental crust crumples and folds, forming **mountains** along the coast.

Revision Questions
Tested

1 Copy and complete the paragraph below to explain how earthquakes can occur at the boundaries of tectonic plates. Choose the correct words from this list.

jerking	perpendicular to	temperature
parallel to	pressure	smooth

At plate boundaries, plates can move _____ each other. The plates often stick and _____ builds up. The sudden release of the plates causes a _____ movement and an earthquake occurs.   **[3 marks]**

2 Describe how the movement of tectonic plates can cause a volcano.   **[6 marks]**

3 a) Copy and complete the table below to show the nature of the main parts of the Earth. One part has already been done for you.

Structure	Nature	Composition
Inner core	Dense solid	Iron and nickel
	Thick and viscous	Silica and minerals
Outer core		
Crust		Basalt

[4 marks]

> ## Exam tip
> Make sure you know the meanings of all the important terms in this section: tectonic plates, crust, mantle and lithosphere. And learn the causes of earthquakes and volcanoes.

b) Northen Ireland has no active volcanoes and seldom experiences severe earthquake activity. Suggest why this is so in terms of plate tectonics.   **[1 mark]**

Go online for the answers
Online

Index